Oxford excellence for the Caribbean

MW00580472

# Principles of Accounts

## SECOND EDITION

Workbook

David Austen

Estellita Louisy

Seema Deosaran-
Pulchan

Theodora Sylvester

OXFORD
UNIVERSITY PRESS

Great Clarendon Street, Oxford, OX2 6DP, United Kingdom

Oxford University Press is a department of the University of Oxford. It furthers the University's objective of excellence in research, scholarship, and education by publishing worldwide. Oxford is a registered trade mark of Oxford University Press in the UK and in certain other countries

British Library Cataloguing in Publication Data

Data available

978-0-19-843730-7

10 9 8 7 6 5 4 3 2 1

Paper used in the production of this book is a natural, recyclable product made from wood grown in sustainable forests. The manufacturing process conforms to the environmental regulations of the country of origin.

Printed in India by Multivista Global Pvt. Ltd

**Acknowledgements**

The publishers would like to thank the following for permission to use their photographs:

Cover image: Joseph Jones/OUP

Although we have made every effort to contact all copyright holders before publication this has not been possible in all cases. If notified, the publisher will rectify any errors or omissions at the earliest opportunity.

Links to third party websites are provided by Oxford in good faith and for information only. Oxford disclaims any responsibility for the materials contained in any third party website referenced in this work.

The exam-style questions that appear in this book have been written by the author. In an examination, the questions may be worded differently.

# Contents

# Improving Your Performance

## Part 1: During your course of study

Here are some questions which you might ask yourself – ideally at the start of your study of principles of accounts but asking the questions at a later stage will also be helpful.

### Question 1

What grade do you want to achieve in principles of accounts to ensure that you are pleased with your result and to ensure that you gain acceptance for the next stage in your education or employment? Setting a specific goal will motivate you and give you something to focus on.

### Question 2

How much time do you spend out of class working on developing your skills in principles of accounts? Maybe you already spend many hours in private study, but if you feel this is not the case, it is a good idea to set yourself some definite plans to increase your study time. This can be done gradually. For example, you could plan to add an extra half an hour to your normal study time for the next few weeks. When you see how you are benefitting from the change, you could add an extra half an hour to this increased time, and so on.

### Question 3

How do you feel when you have received back some work in principles of accounts and you find that you have not done quite as well as you hoped? Many students will, understandably, answer by saying they feel a bit deflated and hope they can get over the disappointment quickly. However, if this is your typical response you could think a little differently. Research shows that this situation is really critical in ensuring that progress is made. Perhaps you could say something like: "Okay, this did not go so well; let me have a look at what I did wrong and learn from my mistakes." Turning a negative experience into something far more positive is likely to make a dramatic difference.

### Question 4

What do you do with all the work you do during your course of study? Perhaps your answer is: "Well, I have it all here somewhere, it just needs sorting out." Many students would find it helpful if they kept a more carefully organised collection of the work they do. Have a separate section for each topic with your notes, all the answers you have prepared together with the questions or at least a reference to where the questions can be found. When it comes to preparing for the examination having a well-organised file will mean you can get on with your revision without wasting time trying to find relevant materials.

## So, at this stage you could be working towards the following position:

- you have a definite goal (grade you would like to achieve)
- you plan to increase your study time
- you have adopted a positive approach to making mistakes, seeing this as a chance to learn and make progress
- you are building up a well-organised file of work which will be invaluable for revision.

# Some practical ideas to help you learn more effectively during your course of study

## Self-assessment

This means that you mark your own work making use of a model answer or mark schemes provided with past examination papers. Research has shown that there are many benefits from doing this, if you carry out the process on a regular and frequent basis, for example:

- you will find out for yourself how well you have done as quickly as you wish after completing a task
- you can get immediate information about any errors or omissions in your answer, so you can start to learn from your mistakes right away
- if you use mark schemes (for example, exam paper mark schemes) you can learn a lot about how marks are allocated to answers by examiners, so that you are better prepared to produce the answers that are expected.

As an alternative to marking your own work, you could pair up with a friend and mark each other's work. The same benefits can be gained from doing this.

## Repairing answers

The most productive thing you can do to improve your performance and increase your rate of progress is to spend time looking closely at any aspect of an answer which was not correct or where something was missing. It is a good idea to spend a little time trying to understand why the model answer differs from your own answer. Try to work out how the right answer was achieved, if you find this a problem ask your teacher or a friend to help you. The critical stage is to add some notes to your answer about how the correct answer was achieved. This will prove far more effective than just saying to yourself "I can see where I went wrong; next time I will try to remember to get that point right". This idea of repairing answers works well for when you are using accounting techniques and also when you are writing descriptions or explanations of accounting terms, accounting ideas, etc.

Here is an example where a student has to prepare an income statement (an extract from the student's answer and the model answer is given).

**Student's answer:**

| | $ | $ |
|---|---|---|
| Revenue | | 400 000 |
| Opening inventory | 10 000 | |
| Purchases | 220 000 | |
| Carriage outwards | 5 000 | |
| | 235 000 | |
| Less closing inventory | 12 000 | |
| | | 223 000 |
| Gross profit | | 177 000 |
| Add: rent received ($8 000 add rent received in advance $1 000) | | 9 000 |
| | | 186 000 |
| Less carriage inwards | | |
| | 2 000 | |

**Model answer:**

| | $ | $ |
|---|---|---|
| Revenue | | 400 000 |
| Opening inventory | 10 000 | |
| Purchases | 220 000 | |
| Carriage inwards | 2 000 | |
| | 232 000 | |
| Less closing inventory | 12 000 | |
| Cost of sales | | 220 000 |
| Gross profit | | 180 000 |
| Add: rent received ($8 000 less rent received in advance $1 000) | | 7 000 |
| | | 187 000 |
| Less carriage outwards | | 5 000 |

The student made two mistakes: mixing up how to treat carriage inwards and outwards, and how to adjust income for income received in advance.

The student could just say "I must remember that carriage costs work the other way around, that I should deduct income received in advance and I should label cost of sales." Far more effective, will be to actually record the corrections on the answer:

| **Student's answer:** | | | | | Notes |
|---|---|---|---|---|---|
| | $ | | $ | | |
| Revenue | | | 400 000 | | |
| Opening inventory | 10 000 | | | | *Carriage inwards goes* |
| Purchases | 220 000 | | | | *in the trading section* |
| Carriage ~~outwards~~ **inwards** | ~~5 000~~ | 2 000 | | | |
| | ~~235 000~~ | 232 000 | | | |
| Less closing inventory | | 12 000 | | | |
| Cost of sales | | | ~~223 000~~ | 220 000 | *Cost of sales should be labelled* |
| Gross profit | | | ~~177 000~~ | 180 000 | |
| Add: rent received ($8 000 add less rent received in advance $1 000) | | | ~~9 000~~ | 7 000 | *Income received in advance is deducted as it is income for next year* |
| | | | ~~186 000~~ | 187 000 | |
| Less carriage ~~inwards~~ **outwards** | ~~2 000~~ | 5 000 | | | *Carriage outwards goes in the profit and loss section* |

# Why is assessing my own work and then "repairing" answers such a good idea?

International research has shown that this approach carried out systematically will make a big difference to what an individual can gain from all the practical work which is carried out during a course of study. In some cases students have improved their performance by several grades!

In the illustration the student has focused attention on how carriage charges are recorded, how an adjustment is made to income, and how to correctly label a figure in the income statement. If this process is repeated every time these kinds of error occur, then very soon the student will have absorbed these points about a correct answer. Remember each correction you make represents a step – maybe just a small step – towards improving performance.

# Part 2: Before the examination

## Revision

This is where your course file will be of great value, particularly if it is comprehensive and well organised. The key to successful revision is to actually answer (or re-answer) questions, not just to look through answers prepared in the past. So, try reworking a question on each topic you feel less than confident about. Make sure you have access to a model answer, or maybe a corrected answer, to each of these questions so that if you get stuck you can check up on the right answer – avoid using model answers until you really have to. Try doing some questions under strict time conditions too – and answer the whole question, don't skip the prose response sections. As part of your revision, check through the syllabus to make sure you have covered everything.

## Using past examination papers

Practising on past examination papers will make a lot of difference to your confidence and to your awareness of what to expect in the examination room. Use the mark schemes not only to check and "repair" your work, but also to help you gain an understanding of what the examiners are looking for. In the case of prose answers, for example, you will gain an appreciation of the length of answer required. Many exam candidates' prose answers are too brief and therefore score badly, or are too lengthy, which means candidates have wasted valuable time.

# Part 3: The examination

Here are some ideas which should help you improve the quality of your answers.

## Time allocation

Try to divide up the time available for the questions in proportion to the marks available. Try to avoid overrunning on any one question as it simply means you will have to rush on another. Remember that you usually earn marks more quickly at the beginning of your answer and rather more slowly at the end.

## Read the question

Do check that you have read the actual question requirements carefully, it is so easy to waste time by providing information which is not required, or missing out some vital element expected by the examiner. For example, do provide an account if the question asks for it. It is surprising to learn that some candidates think that a calculation will suffice when an account is required. In the case of prose questions, do not give a one-word answer if the question asks for an explanation. An explanation requires at least a sentence or two, i.e. some development, so that you demonstrate a good understanding of the subject matter of the question. Go through the question data over and over again. For example, some questions contain a lot of information – so it would be all too easy to overlook an item in a trial balance or an adjustment listed in some notes following a trial balance.

## Workings

Showing detailed calculations is a crucial element in so many answers, so it is vital that you do not leave the examiner to guess how you obtained a particular figure. Take the trouble to make your workings easy to follow. It is good practice to avoid providing a string of figures – a more-carefully labelled list of figures is much more helpful. Students who have got used to providing detailed workings throughout their course of study are far less likely to forget about this when it comes to the stresses of the actual examination. In some cases there can be marks allocated to workings, which can be lost if the workings are omitted and the answer to the calculation is incorrect.

## Matters of detail

Preparing and balancing an account: it is important to give accurate dates and correct narratives when preparing ledger accounts. Make a point of stating the year on each side of the account before you make any further entries. Always bring down the closing balance. The balance brought down should be dated for the beginning of the next period. Many students are not very well skilled in the technique of balancing accounts.

## Presentation and headings

There are very strict rules about the presentation of financial statements which you must follow. These rules have been developed to ensure that users are given clear and precise information. If available, give the name of the business first. Always avoid using abbreviations in headings. Many students spoil otherwise good answers by using y/e (instead of year ended) or reducing the date to a few letters such as Dec (for December), for example. Do not use GP, CoS, NP for labels within an income statement; always write labels in full. Under exam pressure it is quite likely that you will be rushed for time and that you will want to make changes to your answers. Try to ensure that all of your work is legible, however rushed you are. A common problem is that some students write a new figure over an existing figure, and it becomes very difficult or almost impossible to determine exactly what was intended.

## Prose answers

Aim to be as precise in writing your answers to questions requiring a prose response as you would be with numerical work. Make a point of using correct accounting terminology and avoid vagueness. For example, it is easy to spoil an answer by not quite using the right terms: profit (when you mean gross profit); assets (when you mean current assets); profit will be affected (when you mean profit will be increased). Sometimes you will be asked to explain the difference between two accounting terms. It is important to refer to both elements in your answer. For example, if you are asked to explain the difference between trade and cash discount, a weak answer could be "trade discount is given for bulk buying; cash discount is not". Much better to say: "trade discount is given for bulk buying; cash discount is given for prompt payment."

# 1 Accounting as a profession

💬 **Introduction**

In this chapter there are questions to test your understanding of:
- the concept of accounting
- the users of accounting information
- careers in accounting
- ethical issues in accounting.

## Paper 1 questions

1. Which of the following is the main role of a bookkeeper?

    A   preparing end of year financial statements
    B   preparing forecasts and budgets
    C   preparing day-to-day records of transactions
    D   preparing tax returns

2. Which of the following skills will be required when applying for a position as a bookkeeper?

    I.   ability to use accounting software packages
    II.  making tax assessments
    III. preparing records of inventory

    A   I and II only
    B   I and III only
    C   II and III only
    D   I, II and III

3. Which of the following is the main role of an accountant?

    A   summarising the financial position of a business
    B   entering details from source documents
    C   making payroll calculations
    D   preparing the accounts of customers and suppliers

4. Which of the following would be considered as internal stakeholders of a business?

    I.   the owner
    II.  customers
    III. employees

    A   I and II only
    B   I and III only
    C   II and III only
    D   I, II and III

5. Which of the following are ethical principles of accounting?

    **I.** confidentiality

    **II.** integrity

    **III.** trustworthiness

        **A** I and II only

        **B** I and III only

        **C** II and III only

        **D** I, II and III

## Paper 2 questions

6. State **two** tasks you expect a bookkeeper to be responsible for.

7. Outline the purpose of accounting.

8. List **three** qualities required of an accountant.

9. Distinguish between the work of a financial accountant and a management accountant.

10. Define the term "bookkeeping".

11. Explain what is meant by the ethical accounting principle "confidentiality".

### Guidance

In questions 6–11 you will notice that you are asked to state, outline, list, distinguish between, define and explain. These are all words used in examination questions, so it is important that you know what is required in each case. Some words are used to just test your knowledge (factual recall) and require just a one-word answer or phrase; state, outline and list are in this category. "Distinguish between" also tests your knowledge but it is important that you make a statement about each element in the question (in this case you must make a statement about a financial accountant and another statement about a management accountant). The word "define" also tests your knowledge, but it is more demanding because you must give a really precise answer; usually this will require at least one sentence. The requirement to "explain" is also more demanding because it tests your understanding as well as your knowledge. You should write several sentences and develop your answer by building on what you have already said, perhaps giving an example to show that you understand the basic idea(s) being tested in the question.

**Accounting as a system**

> ### Introduction
>
> In this chapter there are questions to test your understanding of:
> * accounting concepts
> * the accounting cycle
> * accounting features of various business organisations
> * technology and accounting
> * the statement of financial position (balance sheet)
> * the effect of transactions on a statement of financial position (balance sheet).

## Paper 1 questions

1.  The owner of a business does not record the costs of running his home in the same accounting system that he uses for his business affairs.

    Which accounting concept is being applied by the owner of the business?

    A   accruals (matching)

    B   consistency

    C   prudence

    D   separate entity

2.  Which accounting concepts are applied when calculating the profit made by a business?

    I.   accruals (matching)

    II.  consistency

    III. prudence

    A   I and II only

    B   I and III only

    C   II and III only

    D   I, II and III

3.  Which of the following steps should follow from entering details in books of original entry in the accounting cycle?

    A   drawing up financial statements

    B   posting to ledger accounts

    C   processing source documents

    D   using control systems

4.  Which **one** of the following organisations benefits from limited liability for debts?

    A   public company

    B   non-trading organisation

    C   partnership

    D   sole trader

**5.** Which of the following is a correct version of the accounting equation?

I.   Assets = Capital + Liabilities

II.  Capital = Assets − Liabilities

III. Liabilities = Capital − Assets

    **A**   I and II only

    **B**   I and III only

    **C**   II and III only

    **D**   I, II and III

**6.** Which of the following correctly lists a business's assets?

    **A**   accounts payable, cash in hand, furniture

    **B**   cash at bank, equipment, bank loan

    **C**   inventory, accounts receivable, premises

    **D**   machinery, bank overdraft, fittings

**7.** A business has opened with the following:

|  | $ |
|---|---|
| Cash in hand | 1 000 |
| Accounts payable | 2 000 |
| Bank loan | 5 000 |
| Inventory | 6 000 |
| Delivery vehicle | 12 000 |

What is the business's capital?

    **A**   $12 000

    **B**   $16 000

    **C**   $22 000

    **D**   $26 000

**8.** The owner of a business has taken out a loan from the bank.

Which of the following correctly states the effect on the accounting equation?

| **A** | +A | −A |
|---|---|---|
| **B** | +A | +L |
| **C** | +L | −A |
| **D** | +L | −C |

**9.** The owner of a business has purchased a delivery vehicle on credit.

Which of the following correctly states the effect on the accounting equation?

| **A** | +A | −A |
|---|---|---|
| **B** | +A | +L |
| **C** | +C | +A |
| **D** | +L | −C |

**10.** The owner of a business made his motor vehicle available for business use.

Which of the following correctly states the effect on the accounting equation?

| A | +A | −A |
|---|----|----|
| B | +A | +L |
| C | +C | +A |
| D | −L | +C |

# Paper 2 questions

## 11. Technology and accounting

Angelo has been in business for a number of years and has kept manual accounting records. A friend has suggested that he would find it much easier if he switched to using computerised accounting records.

a. State the name of an accounting software package.
b. Explain **two** benefits which could arise if Angelo used computerised accounting records.
c. Explain **two** possible disadvantages of changing to a computerised system.

### Guidance
Remember that just a very short response is required when a question asks you to "state", but you must provide a much more developed answer to demonstrate your understanding when a question asks you to "explain".

## 12. The accounting cycle and accounting equation

a. State what is meant by the term "accounting cycle".
b. Copy and complete the following table by filling in the missing figures indicated by the question marks.

|       | Assets | Capital | Liabilities |
|-------|--------|---------|-------------|
|       | $      | $       | $           |
| i.    | 18 000 | ?       | 4 000       |
| ii.   | 274 000 | 251 000 | ?          |
| iii.  | ?      | 93 500  | 17 200      |

### Guidance
It is always worthwhile just spending a little extra time when you have completed an answer requiring calculations to double check your arithmetic is correct.

13. **Preparing a simple classified statement of financial position (balance sheet) (order of permanence)**

   **a.** Define the term "asset".

   Armstrong owns a sports shop, "Gold Medal Sports". On 31 December 2018 the following information was available about his business.

   |  | $ |
   |---|---|
   | Accounts payable | 14 400 |
   | Accounts receivable | 11 720 |
   | Bank loan (repayable 2022) | 15 000 |
   | Cash at bank | 8 320 |
   | Cash in hand | 560 |
   | Equipment | 8 500 |
   | Furniture and fittings | 7 300 |
   | Inventory | 14 990 |
   | Shop premises | 56 500 |

   **b.** Calculate the business's capital on 31 December 2018.

   **c.** Prepare a statement of financial position (balance sheet) at 31 December 2018, setting out the details in order of permanence.

   **Guidance**

   It is important to remember that a statement of financial position (balance sheet) is a formal document so it must be well presented.

14. **Preparing a simple classified statement of financial position (balance sheet) (order of liquidity)**

   **a.** Define the term "liability".

   Ursula owns a fashion store, "Looking Good". On 31 October 2018 the following information was available about this business.

   |  | $ |
   |---|---|
   | Accounts payable | 11 240 |
   | Accounts receivable | 2 820 |
   | Bank overdraft | 3 970 |
   | Cash in hand | 440 |
   | Equipment | 5 400 |
   | Inventory | 18 350 |
   | Loan from JJL Finance (repayable January 2019) | 7 500 |
   | Shop furniture and fittings | 11 900 |

   **b.** Calculate the business's capital on 31 December 2018.

   **c.** Prepare a statement of financial position (balance sheet) at 31 December 2018, setting out the details in order of liquidity.

15. **The effect of transactions on items in a statement of financial position (balance sheet)**

Copy and complete the following table with figures showing the progressive effect of each transaction on the various components.

|  |  | Assets | Capital | Liabilities |
|---|---|---|---|---|
|  |  | $ | $ | $ |
|  | Starting figures | 92 000 | 81 000 | 11 000 |
| a. | Purchased a vehicle, $17 000 and paid by cheque |  |  |  |
| b. | Paid a credit supplier $3 000 by cheque |  |  |  |
| c. | Sold some unwanted furniture on credit, $300 |  |  |  |
| d. | The owner withdrew cash $2 000 for private use |  |  |  |
| e. | Purchased equipment on credit, $4 700 |  |  |  |
| f. | The owner made her own motor vehicle, $14 800, available for business use |  |  |  |

16. **Recording transactions using statements of financial position (balance sheets)**

On 1 February 2018 Lloyd opened a fitness centre with the following assets and liabilities:

|  | $ |
|---|---|
| Furniture and equipment | 13 000 |
| Cash at bank | 5 500 |
| Cash in hand | 600 |
| Bank loan | 7 200 |

a. Calculate the business's capital on 1 February 2018 and prepare a simple unclassified statement of financial position (balance sheet) at that date.

The following transactions occurred during February 2018:

Feb    5 Purchased additional equipment $4 000 on credit

        9 Lloyd withdrew cash $300 for private use

     11 Transferred cash $200 to the bank account

     15 Paid the account payable $2 500 by cheque

     18 Arranged an additional bank loan of $2 000; the funds were transferred to the business's bank account

     23 Some equipment which had proved unsatisfactory was sold on credit for $900

**b.** Prepare a simple unclassified statement of financial position (balance sheet) after each transaction.

## Guidance
Make sure the totals of the statement of financial position (balance sheet) agree after you record each transaction. If they do not agree, rethink the entries you have made.

# 3 Books of original entry

> ## Introduction
>
> In this chapter there are questions to test your understanding of:
> - source documents
> - purchases book
> - sales book
> - purchases returns book
> - sales returns book
> - cash book
> - petty cash book
> - general journal
> - cash and trade discounts.

## Paper 1 questions

1. Which of the following source documents will be required in order to make entries in the sales book?

   A credit note
   B delivery note
   C invoice
   D receipts

2. Which source document is used to prepare the purchases returns book?

   A credit note issued
   B credit note received
   C invoice issued
   D invoice received

3. Which source document is used to make debit entries in the cash column of a cash book?

   A bank statement
   B paying-in slip counterfoil
   C petty cash voucher
   D till rolls

4. A customer was sold goods on credit. The goods were recorded in the supplier's price list with a value of $4 000. The customer was offered a trade discount of 25% and a cash discount of 5% for prompt payment.

   What amount should be recorded in the sales book?

   A $2 800     B $2 850     C $3 000     D $4 000

**5.** Which of the following should be recorded in general journal?

    **A**   payment to the supplier of a non-current asset

    **B**   purchase of goods on credit

    **C**   returns of goods previously purchased on credit

    **D**   sale of a non-current asset on credit

**6.** A petty cash book has an imprest of $60. At the end of a month a cheque was received for $40 to restore the imprest.

How much was spent by the petty cashier during the month?

    **A**  $20      **B**  $40      **C**  $60      **D**  $100

**7.** The amount of "$250" and "cash" was recorded on a cheque counterfoil.

What entries should be made based on this information?

|   | Debit | Credit |
|---|-------|--------|
| A | Cash | Sales |
| B | Bank | Sales |
| C | Cash | Bank |
| D | Bank | Cash |

**8.** Which of the following should **not** be recorded in the general journal?

    **A**   correcting an error in the sales ledger

    **B**   entries to open a new set of books of account

    **C**   purchase of a non-current asset by cheque

    **D**   transfer of wages to the income statement

**9.** The following totals appeared in the discount columns of a cash book.

| Dr |  |  |  |  |  |  | Cr |
|----|-----------|------|------|---|-----------|------|------|
|  | Discounts | Cash | Bank |  | Discounts | Cash | Bank |
|  | $ | $ | $ |  | $ | $ | $ |
|  | 230 |  |  |  | 170 |  |  |

What entries should be made in the general ledger?

|   | Debit | Credit |
|---|-------|--------|
| A | Discounts allowed $170 | Discounts received $230 |
| B | Discounts allowed $230 | Discounts received $170 |
| C | Discounts received $170 | Discounts allowed $230 |
| D | Discounts received $230 | Discounts allowed $170 |

**10.** A petty cash book has a weekly imprest of $80. During a recent week $50 was spent on petty cash expenses.

How much should be received in order to restore the imprest at the end of the week?

    **A**  $30      **B**  $50      **C**  $80      **D**  $130

# Paper 2 questions

## 11. Preparing purchases, sales and returns books from source documents

a. State **one** reason why a business may offer a trade discount to credit customers.

b. Describe **one** reason why a business might receive a debit note.

Cherise sells electrical equipment. She has provided the following details from the source documents for June 2018.

| June | 5 | Invoice 6732 received from TLZ Ltd for goods $870 |
| | 8 | Invoice 449 issued to Leon's Retail Store for goods list price $1 600 less 20% trade discount |
| | 11 | Credit note 102 received from TLZ Ltd for goods $60, not as ordered |
| | 14 | Invoice 3732 received from PXJ Ltd for goods $5 400 less 33 1/3% trade discount |
| | 19 | Credit note 39 issued to Leon's Retail store for goods sold on 8 June with a list price of $160 |
| | 23 | Invoice 450 issued to Hightown Stores for goods list price $3 600 less 25% trade discount |

c. Prepare the following books of original entry for June 2018:
- purchases book
- sales book
- purchases returns book
- sales returns book.

### Guidance

It is important to remember that where there is a trade discount, only the net amount is recorded in the books of account. When working out a discount of 33 1/3%, divide the amount by three. Do not multiply by 33.33%, as this will give a slightly inaccurate result.

## 12. Preparing a three-column cash book from source documents

a. State how a credit customer would be informed of the possibility of a cash discount on a particular sale.

b. Explain why a cash discount received is both beneficial and a disadvantage to a business.

Anthony maintains a three-column cash book for his business. On 1 August 2018 the business had cash in hand of $175 and a bank overdraft of $1 560. During August 2018 the following documents were used to make entries in the cash book.

| Aug | 3 | Receipt | General expenses $45 |
| | 5 | Cheque counterfoil | Drawings $320 |

| 9 | Paying-in slip counterfoil | Account receivable, TBR Ltd, $1 350 (in settlement of their account balance, $1 400) |
|---|---|---|
| 14 | Till roll | Sales $3 460 |
| 16 | Paying-in slip counterfoil | Cash $3 300 |
| 19 | Cheque counterfoil | Account payable, GK Wholesale, $760, in settlement of their account less a 5% cash discount |
| 25 | Receipt | Account payable, Carnell Peters, $80 |
| 27 | Cheque counterfoil | Cash $420 |

c. Prepare Anthony's three-column cash book for August 2018. Balance the cash book on 31 August 2018.

> **Guidance**
>
> Care is required when calculating the cash discount on 19 August. It is important to note that the $760 paid is after deducting the discount, so the amount paid represents 95% of the original amount owing. When balancing the cash book it is a common error to try and balance the discount columns. Discount columns are totalled because they memorandum records of discounts and are not part of the double entry.

### 13. Preparing a petty cash book

a. State what is meant by the term "imprest" when referring to petty cash systems.

b. Explain the purpose of analysis columns when preparing a petty cash book.

Nia makes uses of a petty cash book which has a monthly imprest of $200. The petty cash book has analysis columns for: travel expenses, stationery, fuel and postage. The following information is available for October 2018.

| Oct | 1 | Balance of petty cash in hand $63 |
|---|---|---|
| | 2 | Cheque received to restore imprest |
| | 3 | Paid travel expenses of employee $17.20 |
| | 5 | Purchased stationery $11.80 |
| | 8 | Refuelling of delivery vehicle $40.30 |
| | 12 | Postage charges $8.40 |
| | 14 | Taxi fare paid for manager $18.10 |
| | 18 | Printer paper $12.20 |
| | 23 | Postage $5.60 |
| | 28 | Refuelling of delivery vehicle $33.50 |

c. Prepare Nia's petty cash book for October 2018. Balance the petty cash book on 31 October 2018.

## Guidance

A common mistake is to make an entry for $200 on 2 October. The cheque will be sufficient to result in a total balance of $200 bearing in mind there is already $63 in petty cash. It is advisable to make entries for each payment in both the payment column and the analysis column simultaneously as you work through the list of transactions. At the end of the month total the analysis columns, but balance the petty cash account.

### 14. Preparing entries in a general journal

a. Describe the purpose of the general journal.

b. Give **one** example of a source document which would be recorded in a business's general journal.

Benjamin opened his business on 1 April 2018. The following transactions occurred which were to be recorded in his business's general journal.

| April | 1 | Business opened with cash at bank $4 470, furniture and equipment $11 840, bank loan $5 000 |
| | 12 | Purchased additional furniture on credit from RK Supplies Ltd, $5 600 |
| | 21 | Corrected an error made when recording the payment of wages $120 in cash. An incorrect amount of $130 had been entered in the accounts |
| | 25 | Returned some of the additional furniture purchased on credit from RK Supplies Ltd on12 April, $630. |

c. Prepare entries in Benjamin's general journal to record these transactions.

## Guidance

Don't forget to include a narrative with each journal entry (unless a question states that these are not required).When making entries to correct an error a good tip is to sketch the ledger accounts and record the errors made. This way it is easier to visualise the entries required to make the corrections.

### 15. Preparing some books of original entry from a list of transactions

a. State the purpose of books of original entry.

Rhashan owns Grove General Stores. His business's accounting system includes the following books of original entry:

- purchases book
- sales book
- purchases returns book
- sales returns book
- three-column cash book
- general journal.

On 1 February 2018 there was cash in hand $380, cash at bank $1 990. The following transactions occurred during February 2018.

| Feb | 2 | Invoice | Received from PT Supplies Ltd for $4 400 less 20% trade discount |
|---|---|---|---|
| | 5 | Cheque counterfoil | FQ Wholesale for $1 600 less a cash discount of 2.5% |
| | 8 | Till rolls | Sales $3 490 |
| | 9 | Credit note | Received from PT Supplies Ltd for goods purchased on 2 February with a list price of $150 which had been damaged in transit |
| | 14 | Invoice | For some new shop fittings from Hightown Shop Fitters Ltd $3 350 |
| | 18 | Paying-in slip | Cash $3 000 |
| | 19 | Invoice | Issued to Sharon Williams for goods $820 |
| | 20 | Receipt | Office expenses $80 |
| | 22 | Letter | Received from FQ Wholesale stating that the cash discount deducted when payment was made on 5 February had been cancelled as the deadline for settlement had passed |
| | 23 | Credit note | Issued to Sharon Williams for goods $40 which were not as ordered |
| | 28 | Paying-in slip | Payment by Sharon Williams for the amount outstanding for this month's transactions less a 5% cash discount |

b. Prepare the books of original entry for February 2018. Balance the cash book on 28 February 2018.

**Guidance**

You might find it helpful before preparing your answer to work through the list and pencil in which book of original entry will be required to record each transaction. Don't forget to deduct the trade discount when recording the transaction on 9 February.

**4**

# Ledgers and the trial balance

> ## 💬 Introduction
>
> In this chapter there are questions to test your understanding of:
> - real, nominal and personal accounts
> - general, sales and purchases ledgers
> - posting from books of original entry
> - balancing and closing accounts
> - interpreting entries and balances
> - trial balances.

## Paper 1 questions

1.  Which of the following is a real account?

    **A**  cash                       **B**  drawings

    **C**  sales                      **D**  wages

2.  Which of the following is a nominal account?

    **A**  account receivable

    **B**  delivery vehicle

    **C**  insurance

    **D**  inventory

3.  A bookkeeper is posting the totals of a purchases returns book and a sales book. Which of the following entries is correct?

    |   | Debit | Credit |
    |---|---|---|
    | **A** | Purchases returns<br>Sales | |
    | **B** | Purchases returns | Sales |
    | **C** | | Purchases returns<br>Sales |
    | **D** | Sales | Purchases returns |

4.  A bookkeeper is posting the total of the purchases book and sales returns book. Which of the following entries is correct?

    |   | Debit | Credit |
    |---|---|---|
    | **A** | Purchases<br>Sales returns | |
    | **B** | Purchases | Sales returns |
    | **C** | | Sales returns<br>Purchases |
    | **D** | Sales returns | Purchases |

5. Elsa returned goods sold on credit to her by Marva. How should this transaction be recorded in the books of Marva?

|   | Debit | Credit |
|---|---|---|
| **A** | Elsa | Sales returns |
| **B** | Elsa | Purchases returns |
| **C** | Sales returns | Elsa |
| **D** | Purchases returns | Elsa |

6. The following is an extract from a business's cash book.

| Dr | Cash book (extract) | | | |
|---|---|---|---|---|
|   | Discounts | Cash | Bank |   |
|   | $ | $ | $ |   |
| Total | 364 | | | |

How should the discounts total of $364 be posted to the general ledger?

|   | Debit | Credit |
|---|---|---|
| **A** | Discounts allowed |   |
| **B** | Discounts received |   |
| **C** |   | Discounts allowed |
| **D** |   | Discounts received |

7. The following account appeared in Judith's purchases ledger

| Dr | | Gareth Kenton | | Cr |
|---|---|---|---|---|
|   | $ |   |   | $ |
| Returns | 400 | Balance b/d |   | 3 400 |
| Bank | 2 850 | |   |   |
| Discounts | 150 | |   |   |

Which of the following statements is correct about the transactions recorded in this account?

**A** there were discounts allowed and sales returns
**B** there were discounts allowed and purchases returns
**C** there were discounts received and sales returns
**D** there were discounts received and purchases returns

8. Calvin's account in Anika's sales ledger has a credit balance.

Which of the following statements is true in describing the credit balance?

**A** Anika is in debt to Calvin
**B** Anika has sold goods to Calvin
**C** Calvin is in debt to Anika
**D** Calvin has sold goods to Anika

9. Which of the following statements about a trial balance are correct?

   I  a trial balance lists all the balances in the books of account
   II  if the trial balance totals agree the ledger accounts are error free
   III  trial balance details are useful for preparing financial statements

   | | | | |
   |---|---|---|---|
   | **A** | I and II only | **C** | II and III only |
   | **B** | I and III only | **D** | I, II and III |

10. Which of the following lists correctly how account balances should be recorded in a trial balance?

| | Debit | Credit |
|---|---|---|
| **A** | Discounts allowed<br>Carriage inwards | Discounts received<br>Sales returns |
| **B** | Carriage outwards<br>Drawings | Discounts allowed<br>Revenue |
| **C** | Purchases returns<br>Discounts allowed | Bank loan<br>Sales returns |
| **D** | Drawings<br>Sales returns | Bank overdraft<br>Discounts received |

# Paper 2 questions

## 11. Posting entries from purchases, sales and returns books

a. Distinguish between a real account and a nominal account.
   Angelo owns a wholesale business. The following are extracts from some of his business's books of original entry for August 2018.

|  |  | Purchases book |  | Page 17 |
|---|---|---|---|---|
|  |  |  | Folio | $ |
| Aug | 5 | XQ Manufacturers |  | 3 650 |
|  | 14 | Island Autos |  | 4 490 |
|  | 23 | XQ Manufacturers |  | 1 830 |
|  | 31 | Total purchases |  | 9 970 |

|  |  | Sales book |  | Page 43 |
|---|---|---|---|---|
|  |  |  | Folio | $ |
| Aug | 8 | Ford Retail Unit |  | 880 |
|  | 16 | Woodland Stores |  | 3 170 |
|  | 27 | Ford Retail Unit |  | 2 390 |
|  | 31 | Total sales |  | 6 440 |

|  |  | Purchases returns book |  | Page 11 |
|---|---|---|---|---|
|  |  |  | Folio | $ |
| Aug | 11 | XQ Manufacturers |  | 490 |
|  | 20 | Island Autos |  | 380 |
|  | 31 | Total purchases returns |  | 810 |

|  | Sales returns book | | Page 9 |
|---|---|---|---|
|  |  | Folio | $ |
| Aug | 12 Ford Retail Unit |  | 220 |
|  | 23 Woodland Stores |  | 170 |
|  | 31 Total sales returns |  | 390 |

**b.** Post the details from these books of original entry to the relevant accounts in the general, purchases and sales ledgers. Include folio references in the entries.

---

**Guidance**

In each account take your time to record the correct information about each transaction. This should include the date, a narrative, a folio reference as well as the amount. Record the year at the beginning of each date column. The folio reference should use the initial of the book of original entry and the page number, e.g. PB17.

---

**12. Preparing personal accounts from books of original entry**

**a.** State the purpose of folio references.

The following are extracts from the books of original entry for the business owned by James Devon.

|  | Sales book | | Page 59 |
|---|---|---|---|
|  |  | Folio | $ |
| Sept | 5 RJ Ltd |  | 590 |
|  | 14 Beacon Stores |  | 1310 |
|  | 23 RJ Ltd |  | 840 |
|  | 28 Beacon Stores |  | 1960 |
|  | 30 Total sales |  | 4700 |

|  | Sales returns book | | Page 11 |
|---|---|---|---|
|  |  | Folio | $ |
| Sept | 11 RJ Ltd |  | 30 |
|  | 22 Beacon Stores |  | 110 |
|  | 30 Total sales returns |  | 140 |

| Dr | | | Cash book (extracts) | | | | Page 44 |
|---|---|---|---|---|---|---|---|
|  |  |  | Folio | Discounts | Cash | Bank |  |
|  |  |  |  | $ | $ | $ |  |
| Sept | 8 | RJ Ltd |  | 4 | 76 |  |  |
|  | 24 | Beacon Stores |  | 28 |  | 1372 |  |
|  | 29 | RJ Ltd |  | 70 |  | 1330 |  |

| General Journal | | | Page 8 | |
|---|---|---|---|---|
| | | | Dr | Cr |
| | | | $ | $ |
| Sept | 28 | Beacon Stores | 28 | |
| | | Discounts allowed | | 28 |
| | | Cancellation of cash discount as deadline not met | | |

On 1 September 2018 the balances in sales ledger accounts were:

| | $ |
|---|---|
| Beacon Stores | 1 400 |
| RJ Ltd | 80 |

**b.** Calculate the percentage cash discount allowed to the following.
  **i.** RJ Ltd.
  **ii.** Beacon Stores.
**c.** Prepare the sales ledger accounts of RJ Ltd and Beacon Stores. Balance the accounts on 30 September 2018. Include folio references.

## Guidance

You should post the entries to the two accounts in strict date order. It might be helpful to tick each item as you post it to the accounts. When balancing the accounts, remember to bring any balance down; the brought down balance should be dated for the first day of the next month.

13. **Preparing a trial balance**

Trial balances are used to check the arithmetical accuracy of the double-entry records, but their usefulness is limited.
**a.** Explain why the usefulness of trial balances is limited.
**b.** State **one** other benefit of preparing a trial balance, other than checking the arithmetical accuracy of the double-entry records.

Nerissa has extracted the following list of balances from her business's books of account at 30 November 2018.

| | $ | | $ |
|---|---|---|---|
| Bank overdraft | 380 | Loan from TZ Finance | 8 000 |
| Carriage inwards | 710 | Non-current assets | 48 500 |
| Carriage outwards | 450 | Petty cash in hand | 30 |
| Capital | 47 650 | Purchases | 127 900 |
| Discounts allowed | 550 | Sales returns | 840 |
| Discounts received | 420 | Purchases returns | 630 |
| Drawings | 18 320 | Revenue | 169 900 |
| General expenses | 7 280 | Wages | 22 400 |

**c.** Prepare a trial balance at 30 November 2018.

## 14. Interpreting accounts

The following accounts appeared in the ledger of the business owned by Shenika.

Purchases Ledger

| Dr | | | | | Andrew Grant | | | | Cr |
|---|---|---|---|---|---|---|---|---|---|
| 2018 | | | | $ | 2018 | | | | $ |
| July | 21 | Returns | ROB5 | 80 | July | 1 | Balance | b/d | 4920 |
| | 28 | Bank | CB14 | 3800 | | 14 | Purchases | PB7 | 3860 |
| | 28 | Discounts | CB14 | 200 | | | | | |
| | 31 | Balance | c/d | 4700 | | | | | |
| | | | | 8780 | | | | | 8780 |
| | | | | | Aug | 1 | Balance | b/d | 4700 |

**a.** Describe each entry made in this purchases ledger account.

Sales Ledger

| Dr | | | | $ | Lisa Marks | | | | Cr |
|---|---|---|---|---|---|---|---|---|---|
| 2018 | | | | $ | 2018 | | | | $ |
| July | 15 | Sales | SB22 | 60 | July | 25 | Cash | CB14 | 57 |
| | | | | | | 25 | Discounts | CB14 | 3 |
| | | | | 60 | | | | | 60 |

**b.** Describe each entry made in this sales ledger account.

General Ledger

| Dr | | | | | Non-current assets | | | | Cr |
|---|---|---|---|---|---|---|---|---|---|
| 2018 | | | | $ | 2018 | | | | $ |
| July | 1 | Balance | b/d | 27500 | July | 31 | Balance | c/d | 31100 |
| | 27 | HW Stores | J3 | 3600 | | | | | |
| | | | | 31100 | | | | | 31100 |
| Aug | 1 | Balance | b/d | 31100 | | | | | |

**c.** Describe each entry made in this general ledger account.

## 15. Preparing a full set of accounting records up to the trial balance stage

George opened a business on 1 April 2018 with the following assets and liabilities.

|  | $ |
|---|---|
| Cash at bank | 8 000 |
| Non-current assets | 38 000 |
| Bank loan | 12 000 |

**a.** Prepare an opening journal entry to record the business's assets, liability and capital.

During April 2018 the following transactions took place.

| April | |
|---|---|
| 3 | Cashed a cheque for $800 to provide resources for making cash payments |
| 4 | Purchased goods on credit from WV Manufacturers for list price $9 000 less 20% trade discount. |
| 7 | Cash purchases $220 |
| 8 | Returned goods to WV Manufacturers list price $240 purchased on credit on 4 April – the goods were damaged in transit |
| 11 | Sales on credit to Kathy's General Store $1 890 |
| 14 | Drawings by cheque $320 |
| 16 | Purchased additional non-current assets on credit from RTV Supplies, $1 800 |
| 17 | Kathy's General Store returned goods sold on credit on 11 April, $110 – the goods were not as ordered |
| 19 | Paid general expenses in cash $140 |
| 21 | Paid WV Manufacturers by cheque in full settlement of $4 000 of the amount due less a 5% cash discount |
| 23 | Returned some items purchased from RTV Supplies on 16 April, $220 – the items were not as ordered |
| 24 | Cash sales $4 360 |
| 27 | Paid cash into bank $4 000 |
| 28 | Received a cheque, $1 750 from Kathy's General Store in full settlement of the amount due. |

**b.** Record the transactions in the business's books of original entry.
**c.** Post the entries to the general, purchases and sales ledger accounts.
**d.** Prepare a trial balance at 30 April 2018.

### Guidance

This large-scale question tests all the skills relevant to double-entry bookkeeping up to, and including, the trial balance. To help ensure accuracy, be systematic. Work through the transactions in the order given, recording each in the appropriate book of original entry first. Do not forget to total the purchases, sales and returns books and the discount columns in the cash book at the end of the month. When you have recorded all the transactions in the books of original entry, move on to posting to ledger accounts. It is easy to forget to post the totals of the purchases, sales and returns books and the totals of the discount columns.

## Introduction

In this chapter there are questions to test your understanding of:
- a sole trader's income statement
- the effect of net profit or net loss on capital
- classified statements of financial position (balance sheets) in a vertical style
- working capital
- ratios to determine profitability
- ratios to demonstrate the financial position of a business
- making recommendations about a business based on ratio analysis.

## Paper 1 questions

1. Which of the following correctly lists current assets in order of permanence?

    A   accounts receivable, inventory, cash at bank, prepaid expenses
    B   cash at bank, prepaid expenses, accounts receivable, inventory
    C   inventory, accounts receivable, prepaid expenses, cash at bank
    D   prepaid expenses, inventory, accounts receivable, cash at bank

2. A business's statement of financial position includes the following:

    |                      | $      |
    |----------------------|--------|
    | Inventory            | 10 000 |
    | Income in advance    | 1 000  |
    | Bank overdraft       | 3 000  |
    | Accounts receivable  | 9 000  |
    | Accounts payable     | 7 000  |

    What is the business's working capital?

    A   $8 000      B   $10 000      C   $14 000      D   $16 000

3. The following balances were extracted from the books of a sole trader at the end of the business's first year.

    |                   | $      |
    |-------------------|--------|
    | Closing inventory | 16 000 |
    | Carriage inwards  | 3 000  |
    | Purchases         | 45 000 |
    | Revenue           | 88 000 |

    What was the business's gross profit?

    A   $24 000      B   $30 000      C   $56 000      D   $62 000

**4.** The following details relate to a sole trader's business

|                   | $000 |
|-------------------|------|
| Opening inventory | 12   |
| Purchases         | 50   |
| Revenue           | 76   |
| Closing inventory | 8    |

What is the business's rate of inventory turnover?

**A** 2.7 times    **B** 3.8 times    **C** 5.4 times    **D** 7.6 times

**5.** The following balances were extracted from the books of a sole trader at the end of the business's financial year.

|                   | $000 |
|-------------------|------|
| Closing inventory | 25   |
| Opening inventory | 15   |
| Purchases         | 240  |
| Purchases returns | 10   |
| Revenue           | 350  |
| Sales returns     | 5    |

What was the business's gross profit?

**A** $95 000    **B** $105 000    **C** $115 000    **D** $125 000

**6.** The following details are available for a retail business for the year ended 31 December 2018.

|                                                   | $       |
|---------------------------------------------------|---------|
| Carriage inwards                                  | 3 000   |
| Carriage outwards                                 | 5 000   |
| General expenses                                  | 20 000  |
| Closing inventory larger than opening inventory   | 4 000   |
| Purchases                                         | 60 000  |
| Revenue                                           | 100 000 |

Which of the following is a correct statement of the business's gross profit and net profit?

|   | Gross profit | Net profit |
|---|--------------|------------|
|   | $            | $          |
| A | 32 000       | 8 000      |
| B | 33 000       | 16 000     |
| C | 39 000       | 8 000      |
| D | 41 000       | 16 000     |

**7.** What is the formula for calculating mark-up?

   **A** gross profit for the year divided by cost of sales
   **B** gross profit for the year divided by revenue
   **C** net profit for the year divided by cost of sales
   **D** net profit for the year divided by revenue

8. A business's gross profit margin decreased comparing 2018 with 2017. Which of the following would account for this change?

   A   the business held less inventory

   B   there was an increase in the business's running costs

   C   the cost price of a unit decreased

   D   there was a decrease in the selling price of a unit

9. The following details were extracted from a business's statement of financial position (balance sheet): bank overdraft $2 000, inventory $9 000, accounts payable $5 000, accounts receivable $8 000.

   What was the business's acid test ratio (to one decimal place)?

   A   5.8:1          B   2.4:1          C   2.0:1          D 1.1:1

10. On 31 December 2018 a business had non-current assets of $60 000, working capital of $10 000, non-current liabilities of $20 000 and it had made a net profit of $20 000 during the year ended on that date.

    What was the business's return on investment (to one decimal place)?

    A   25.0%          B   28.6%          C   40.0%          D 66.7%

## Paper 2 questions

### 11. Preparing the trading section of a business's income statement

a.  Distinguish between carriage inwards and carriage outwards.

    Grace owns "Mainstreet Fashions". On 30 November 2018 she provided the following details about her business's financial year which ended on that date.

    |                        | $       |
    | ---------------------- | ------- |
    | Carriage inwards       | 3 360   |
    | Carriage outwards      | 4 280   |
    | Discounts allowed      | 1 320   |
    | Discounts received     | 940     |
    | General expenses       | 28 790  |
    | Inventories            |         |
    |     1 December 2017 | 14 400  |
    |     30 November 2018 | 18 310  |
    | Purchases              | 182 650 |
    | Purchases returns      | 2 770   |
    | Revenue                | 281 920 |
    | Sales returns          | 3 210   |

b.  Prepare the trading section of the business's income statement for the year ended 30 November 2018, selecting information from the details above.

> ### Guidance
> The question only requires the trading section of the income statement, so it is important to select the right information from the list of details provided and ignore other items. Don't forget to give the statement a full title. When preparing the cost of sales section record purchases, returns and carriage charges in that order.

## 12. Preparing a complete income statement

Lathan owns "Newtown Cycle Store". On 31 August 2018 the following details were extracted from his business's books of account.

Trial balance (extract) at 31 August 2018

|  | $ | $ |
|---|---|---|
| Carriage outwards | 890 | |
| Discounts | 320 | 210 |
| Electricity charges | 1770 | |
| Inventory, 1 September 2017 | 20320 | |
| Insurance | 640 | |
| Purchases | 112200 | |
| Repairs and maintenance charges | 1830 | |
| Returns | 2290 | 3020 |
| Revenue | | 189940 |
| Salaries | 40400 | |
| Water charges | 1450 | |

On 31 August 2018 the business had a closing inventory valued at $19 330.

a. Prepare the inventory account in the business's general ledger.
b. Prepare an income statement for the year ended 31 August 2018.

### Guidance

In a. remember that it only the opening and closing inventories which are recorded in the ledger account (other transactions involving inventory have separate accounts, e.g. purchases, returns and sales). As well as provided a full title, don't forget to label important subtotals (cost of sales, gross profit, net profit).

## 13. Preparing a classified statement of financial position (balance sheet) using a vertical format

a. Define the following terms:
   i. Non-current asset.
   ii. Current asset.

The following balances remained in the books of Shenika Wholesalers on 30 September 2018.

|  | $ | $ |
|---|---|---|
| Accounts payable | | 14650 |
| Accounts receivable | 8080 | |
| Bank loan (repayable 2021) | | 8300 |
| Buildings | 122000 | |
| Capital at 1 October 2017 | | 198540 |
| Cash at bank | 1260 | |
| Cash in hand | 190 | |
| Delivery vehicles | 28400 | |
| Drawings | 17330 | |

| | | |
|---|---:|---:|
| Furniture and equipment | 9 640 | |
| Inventory | 31 370 | |
| Loan from Antonio (repayable December 2018) | | 600 |
| Net loss for year ended 30 September 2018 | 3 820 | |

b. Prepare a statement of financial position (balance sheet) at 30 September 2018 using a vertical format.

## Guidance

Make sure the statement has a full title and that each subsection is given a subtitle. It is important to notice that there are two loans in the list and that they have quite different repayment dates.

## 14. Preparing financial statements for a sole trader

a. Explain why working capital is important in the operation of a business.

Kamau prepared the following trial balance for his business at the end of its financial year.

East Quay Retail Unit
Trial balance at 30 June 2018

| | Dr $ | Cr $ |
|---|---:|---:|
| Accounts payable | | 11 480 |
| Accounts receivable | 9 980 | |
| Bank overdraft | | 440 |
| Capital | | 70 000 |
| Carriage inwards | 1 160 | |
| Discounts allowed | 350 | |
| Discounts received | | 220 |
| Drawings | 28 470 | |
| General expenses | 3 320 | |
| Insurance | 510 | |
| Inventory, 1 July 2017 | 14 490 | |
| Loan from KLQ Finance (repayable 2022) | | 12 500 |
| Loan interest | 840 | |
| Non-current assets | 85 000 | |
| Purchases | 152 570 | |
| Purchases returns | | 1 040 |
| Revenue | | 246 300 |
| Sales returns | 2 220 | |
| Vehicle running costs | 4 870 | |
| Wages | 38 200 | |
| | 341 980 | 341 980 |

On 30 June 2018 inventory was valued at $12 320.

**b.** Prepare an income statement for the year ended 30 June 2018.

**c.** Prepare a statement of financial position (balance sheet) at 30 June 2018.

> **Guidance**
> Before you prepare the income statement it could be worthwhile looking through the items in the trial balance and beside each one pencilling in where the item will be recorded: T (for trading section of the income statement), P (for profit and loss section of the income statement), S (for the statement of financial position). Make sure your answer is well presented: avoid the use of any abbreviations in the titles or contents of the financial statements.

15. **Calculating ratios based on an income statement**

Suzette owns a shop selling high quality shoes. She has provided the following extract from her latest income statement.

Income statement for the year ended 31 March 2018

| | $ | $ |
|---|---|---|
| Revenue | | 400 000 |
| Opening inventory | 22 000 | |
| Purchases | 244 000 | |
| | 266 000 | |
| Closing inventory | 26 000 | |
| Cost of sales | | 240 000 |
| Gross profit | | 160 000 |
| General expenses | 40 000 | |
| Wages of assistants | 60 000 | |
| | | |
| Net profit | | 60 000 |

**a.** Calculate the following ratios:
- gross profit percentage
- mark-up percentage
- rate of inventory turnover
- net profit percentage
- general expenses to revenue percentage
- wages of assistants to revenue percentage.

> **Guidance**
> When calculating ratios it is a good idea to provide the following information for each ratio: the name of the ratio, the formula for calculating the ratio, the figures extracted from the financial statement, the answer. Don't forget to label each answer correctly, for example with a percentage sign where appropriate.

## 16. Calculating ratios based on a statement of financial position (balance sheet)

Grant owns a retail business. The business's most recent statement of financial position (balance sheet) is shown below.

Statement of financial position (balance sheet)

at 31 December 2018

|  | $ | $ |
|---|---|---|
| Non-current assets |  | 220 000 |
|  |  |  |
| Current assets |  |  |
| Inventory | 17 000 |  |
| Accounts receivable | 14 000 |  |
| Cash at bank | 4 000 |  |
|  | 35 000 |  |
| Current liabilities |  |  |
| Accounts payable | 21 000 |  |
|  |  | 14 000 |
|  |  | 234 000 |
|  |  |  |
| Capital |  |  |
| Opening balance | 200 000 |  |
| Net profit for the year | 52 000 |  |
|  | 252 000 |  |
| Drawings | 18 000 |  |
|  |  | 234 000 |

Additional information:

The business had credit sales of $159 700 and credit purchases of $219 000 for the year ended 31 December 2018.

**a.** Identify the value of the business's working capital at 31 December 2018.

**b.** Calculate the following ratios:
- current ratio
- acid test ratio
- return on investment percentage
- accounts receivable collection period
- accounts payable payment period.

### Guidance

Remember in each case to provide the name of the ratio, formula, data and answer. It is suggested that you work to 2 decimal places for most ratios unless you are told to do otherwise. However, in the case of the accounts receivable collection period and accounts payable payment period it is usual to give your answer as whole days (and always round up the number of days – for example, 33.24 days would give an answer of 34 days).

**17. Comparing a business's performance over several years using income statement ratios; making recommendations**

James has prepared the following table to show ratios for his business for the last three years.

| | Year ended 31 December | | |
|---|---|---|---|
| | 2016 | 2017 | 2018 |
| Gross profit percentage | 30% | 32% | 34% |
| Rate of inventory turnover | 14 times | 13 times | 12 times |
| Net profit percentage | 8% | 7% | 6% |

a. Identify any ratio(s) which show an improvement in the business's performance.
b. Identify any ratio(s) which show a decline in the business's performance.

James is puzzled why the net profit percentage has decreased each year when the gross profit percentage has increased each year.

c. Explain why the net profit percentage has decreased each year.

James would like to improve the business's rate of inventory turnover.

d. Recommend **two** ways in which the ratio could be improved.

**Guidance**

Remember in **c.** that you are asked to explain, so you need to provide more than just a single statement. Think about ways in which you can develop your answer perhaps giving an example to illustrate the point you are making.

**18. Comparing a business's performance over several years using statement of financial position (balance sheet) ratios; making recommendations**

Lisette has calculated the following ratios based on her business's statements of financial position (balance sheets) for the last three years.

| | At 31 December | | |
|---|---|---|---|
| | 2016 | 2017 | 2018 |
| Return on investment | 24% | 26% | 28% |
| Current ratio | 1.3:1 | 1.2:1 | 1.0:1 |
| Acid test ratio | 0.5:1 | 0.6:1 | 0.7:1 |

Lisette is puzzled by the increase in the return on investment because her net profit percentage has decreased steadily over recent years.

a. State **one** reason why the return on investment may have increased despite decreasing profits.
b. Explain what is shown by the trend in the current ratio over the three years.
c. Explain what is shown by the trend in the acid test ratio over the three years.
d. Recommend **two** ways in which the current ratio could be improved.

## Guidance

When making recommendations about how to improve the current ratio it is a common mistake to suggest a transaction which will have no effect. For example, it might seem a good idea to suggest that the current ratio would be improved by increasing inventory. However, this is unlikely to have the desired effect because either the bank balance would decrease (if payment for the goods is made immediately) or current liabilities would increase (if the goods are purchased on credit) and these elements of the transaction would cancel out the effect of the increase in inventory.

19. **Comparing the performance of different businesses**

    The results below are for businesses of a similar size trading in the same types of goods.

    |  | Business A | Business B | Business C |
    |---|---|---|---|
    | Net profit percentage | 18% | 16% | 19% |
    | Current ratio | 1.7:1 | 1.5:1 | 1.4:1 |
    | Accounts receivable collection period | 32 days | 34 days | 30 days |
    | Accounts payable payment period | 32 days | 30 days | 34 days |

    The average current ratio for this type of business is 1.5:1.

    a. Give **two** reasons which would explain why Business A's net profit percentage is higher than that of the other two businesses.

    b. Explain why Business A's current ratio is unsatisfactory.

    c. Explain why Business C's current ratio is unsatisfactory.

    d. Explain why Business B's accounts receivable collection period and accounts payable period is unsatisfactory.

## Guidance

It is a common mistake to think that the higher the current ratio the better. The right level of current assets in relation to current liabilities depends on the type of business For example, the current ratio requirement for a supermarket chain where all sales for cash will be far lower than the current ratio for a wholesaler where sales are likely to be on credit. So it is important to compare the current ratio with the average for the type of business.

## 20. Reporting on the performance of a business and making recommendations

The following information is available for Rosa Dalton's retail business for the last two financial years ended 31 December.

|  | 2017 | 2018 |
|---|---|---|
| Revenue | $400 000 | $450 000 |
| Gross profit | $90 000 | $112 500 |
| Net profit | $50 000 | $48 000 |
| Capital (at start of year) | $250 000 | $260 000 |

a. Calculate the following ratios for 2017 and 2018:
   • gross profit percentage
   • net profit percentage
   • return on investment percentage.
b. Comment on the performance of the business comparing 2018 with 2017.
c. Give **two** recommendations on how the business's performance could be improved.

### Guidance
When commenting on the business's performance it is best to describe any changes that are an improvement for the business (i.e. strengths in performance) and any changes which reveal a decline (i.e. weaknesses in performance). Make a point of explaining why the change is a strength or a weakness.

**Accounting adjustments**

> **Introduction**
>
> In this chapter there are questions to test your understanding of:
> - accounting concepts and adjustments
> - journal and ledger entries to record adjustments
> - bad debts and provisions for doubtful debts
> - depreciation
> - capital and revenue expenditure
> - preparation of financial statements including adjustments.

## Paper 1 questions

1. What is the name of the concept which ensures that profits and asset values are not overstated?

    A   accruals concept
    B   consistency concept
    C   matching concept
    D   prudence concept

2. What is the name of the concept which ensures that accounting policies are applied in the same way each year to ensure financial statements can be compared in a valid way?

    A   accruals concept
    B   consistency concept
    C   matching concept
    D   prudence concept

3. A business made a gross profit of $95 000 during a recent financial year. During the same period payments for expenses totalled $18 000. At the end of the financial year expenses accrued totalled $4 000 and expenses prepaid totalled $6 000. What was the business's net profit for the year?

    A   $67 000      B   $75 000      C   $79 000      D   $87 000

4. The following information is available about a business's recent financial year:

    |  | $ |
    |---|---|
    | Gross profit | 240 000 |
    | Amount received from rent | 8 000 |
    | Payments for expenses | 100 000 |

    At the year end expenses were due but unpaid $5 000; rent received in advance totalled $3 000.

    What was the business's net profit?

    A   $140 000      B   $146 000      C   $150 000      D   $156 000

5. A business has a provision for doubtful debts of $4 000. The draft net profit for the current year is $85 000. However, it has now been discovered that a bad debt of $3 000 should have been written off, and the provision for doubtful debts should have been increased to $5 000.

   What will the business's amended net profit be?

   **A** $80 000    **B** $81 000    **C** $82 000    **D** $83 000

6. A business has a provision for doubtful debts of $1 200. The policy is to maintain the provision at 5% of accounts receivable at each year end. Accounts receivable at the end of the current year total $16 000.

   What journal entry is required to update the provision for doubtful debts?

   |   | Debit | Credit |
   |---|-------|--------|
   | **A** | Income statement $400 | Provision for doubtful debts $400 |
   | **B** | Income statement $800 | Provision for doubtful debts $800 |
   | **C** | Provision for doubtful debts $400 | Income statement $400 |
   | **D** | Provision for doubtful debts $800 | Income statement $800 |

7. Which of the following is a cause of depreciation?

   **I.**   wear and tear

   **II.**  obsolescence

   **III.** inadequacy

       **A**   I and II only

       **B**   I and III only

       **C**   II and III only

       **D**   I, II and III

8. A business owns a non-current asset which cost $60 000. In its second year this asset was depreciated by $12 000.

   What was the business's depreciation policy?

       **A**   20% per annum, reducing balance method

       **B**   25% per annum, reducing balance method

       **C**   20% per annum, straight-line method

       **D**   25% per annum, straight-line method

9. A business owns a delivery vehicle which cost $24 000. The vehicle is depreciated by 25% per annum using the reducing balance method.

   What is the correct journal entry to record depreciation of the delivery vehicle at the end of its second year?

   |   | Debit | Credit |
   |---|-------|--------|
   | **A** | Income statement $4 500 | Provision for depreciation $4 500 |
   | **B** | Income statement $6 000 | Provision for doubtful debts $6 000 |
   | **C** | Provision for doubtful debts $4 500 | Income statement $4 500 |
   | **D** | Provision for doubtful debts $6 000 | Income statement $6 000 |

10. Which of the following is capital expenditure for a furniture retailer?

    A   carriage inwards on new equipment
    B   maintenance charges on premises
    C   repairs to computer equipment
    D   van driver's wages

# Paper 2 questions

11. **Accounting concepts and adjustments to expenses and income**

    When preparing a business's financial statements it is necessary to apply the accruals (matching) concept.

    a.   Explain how the accruals concept is applied to a business's financial statements.

    Karam owns a retail business. The business's financial year ends on 31 August.

    The following amounts were paid and received during the year ended 31 August 2018.

    |  | $ |
    |---|---|
    | Expenses | |
    | Insurance | 4 820 |
    | Wages of assistants | 36 880 |
    | Income | |
    | Loan interest received | 1 450 |
    | Rent received | 3 720 |

    Additional information at 31 August 2018:

    - Insurance $360 was prepaid.
    - Wages of assistants $1 230 was due but unpaid.
    - Loan interest $160 was outstanding.
    - Rent received $490 had been received in advance.

    b.   Prepare journal entries to record the transfers from the four accounts to the business's income statement for the year ended 31 August 2018. (Narratives are **not** required.)
    c.   Prepare ledger accounts to record the details about each of the four items. Balance the accounts at 31 August 2018.
    d.   State how the balance of each of the four ledger accounts will be shown on the business's statement of financial position (balance sheet) at 31 August 2018.

---

## Guidance

When making adjustments it is helpful to remember that any amount which is relevant to the financial year should be included, but any amount which is relevant to the next year should be excluded. In brief the rule is: this year IN, next year OUT.

## 12. Bad debts and provisions for doubtful debts

**a.** Define the term "bad debt".

**b.** Give **two** reasons why a credit customer's account may have to be written off as a bad debt.

Denisha is the owner of wholesale business dealing in shoes and footwear. One of her customers, Hightown Fashions, was sold goods on 23 February 2018. The invoice total was $1,480. On 30 November 2018, Denisha was informed that the amount due from this customer would not be paid.

**c.** Prepare a journal entry to write off the account of Hightown Fashions.

**d.** Prepare the ledger account of Hightown Fashions in Denisha's sales ledger.

Denisha decided that she should create a provision for doubtful debts at 31 December 2018, the business's financial year end.

**e.** State the accounting concepts which are being applied when a business prepares a provision for doubtful debts.

**f.** State the double entry required to create a provision for doubtful debts.

### Guidance

A bad debt is an expense, so the double entry to write off a bad debt must include a debit entry in the bad debt account.

## 13. Provisions for doubtful debts

Patrick created a provision for doubtful debts of $600 at 31 December 2016.

**a.** Describe **two** methods that could have been used to decide the amount of the provision for doubtful debts.

At 31 December 2017 Patrick decided to reduce the provision to $530.

**b.** Prepare a journal entry to record the adjustment to the provision for doubtful debts.

At 31 December 2018 Patrick decided it was necessary to increase the provision for doubtful debts by $250.

**c.** Prepare the provision for doubtful debts account in the books of Patrick's business for each of the years 2016, 2017 and 2018.

### Guidance

It is important to remember that a provision for doubtful debts has a credit balance. It is a common error to credit the provision account with the full amount of the provision each year, rather than make an entry for the amount of the adjustment only.

## 14. Depreciation

a. Explain what is meant by the term "nbv" when applied to a non-current asset.

   Delphine owns a business providing guidance on financial matters. On 1 January 2017 she purchased computer equipment costing $18 000 paying by cheque. Her policy is to depreciate all non-current assets by 20% per annum using the straight-line method. On 1 April 2018 Delphine purchased additional computer equipment costing $14 000 on credit from Technoplus Ltd. The business's financial year ends on 31 December.

b. Prepare a journal entry to record the depreciation of the computer equipment on 31 December 2017.

c. Prepare ledger accounts to record:
   i. Computer equipment
   ii. Provision for depreciation of computer equipment for each of the two years 2017 and 2018.

d. Prepare an extract from the business's statement of financial position (balance sheet) at 31 December 2018 to show how computer equipment would be recorded at this date.

### Guidance

In order to record the correct narrative in the computer equipment account it is important to note that the original equipment was purchased by cheque, but that the additional equipment was purchased on credit. It is recommended that workings are provided for the more complex depreciation charges in 2018.

## 15. Capital and revenue expenditure

a. i. Define the term capital expenditure.
   ii. Give **one** example of capital expenditure.

b. i. Define the term revenue expenditure.
   ii. Give **one** example of revenue expenditure.

   Janard owns a car repair business. Recently he paid two of his staff wages to install some new machinery at the business. Janard does not understand why these wages should be debited to the machinery account in the business's books.

c. Explain why these wages should be debited to the machinery account.

   Janard recently also purchased a delivery vehicle for business use. The following payments were made:

| | $ |
|---|---|
| Insurance of delivery vehicle for year | 740 |
| Delivery vehicle | 22 400 |
| Alterations made to interior of vehicle so that equipment could be stored | 1 800 |
| Name of business, logo, etc. painted on side of vehicle | 600 |

d. State how much of the expenditure listed above should be regarded as:
   i. capital expenditure
   ii. revenue expenditure.

e. Explain why it is important to make sure that payments are correctly identified as either capital expenditure or revenue expenditure.

16. **Preparing income statements including simple adjustments, bad debts, provisions for doubtful debts and depreciation.**

Samara owns the Rainbow Stores, a retail unit in a local shopping centre. She sells goods for cash and on credit.

The following information was available about the business's financial year ended 30 September 2018.

|  | $ |
|---|---|
| Bad debts written off | 410 |
| Carriage outwards | 770 |
| Discounts received | 580 |
| Inventory | |
|     1 October 2017 | 18 490 |
|     30 September 2018 | 19 670 |
| Loan interest received | 380 |
| Non-current assets | |
|     Cost | 84 000 |
|     Provision for depreciation, 1 October 2017 | 33 600 |
| Provision for doubtful debts, 1 October 2017 | 630 |
| Purchases | 117 400 |
| Purchases returns | 820 |
| Rent expense | 11 940 |
| Revenue | 212 000 |
| Wages and salaries | 46 470 |

Additional information:

- Rent $1 840 was prepaid at 30 September 2018.
- Wages and salaries $3 310 were due but unpaid at 30 September 2018.
- Loan interest $80 was due but not yet received at 30 September 2018.
- Depreciation should be provided at 20% per annum on cost of non-current assets.
- The provision for doubtful debts should be maintained at 5% of accounts receivable; these totalled $14 400 at 30 September 2018.

Prepare an income statement for the year ended 30 September 2018.

**17. Preparing a statement of financial position (balance sheet) for a business which has recorded adjustments to expenses and income, depreciation charges and a provision for doubtful debts**

a. Explain the purpose of a provision for doubtful debts.

Garfield has provided the following information at the end of his business's financial year, 31 July 2018. He has already prepared the business's income statement for the year ended on that date.

|  | $ |
|---|---|
| Accounts payable | 10 260 |
| Accounts receivable | 7 400 |
| Bank overdraft | 1 090 |
| Capital | 84 000 |
| Drawings | 26 840 |
| General expenses due but unpaid | 450 |
| Insurance paid in advance | 380 |
| Inventory | 11 730 |
| Net profit for the year | 46 910 |
| Non-current assets |  |
| Cost | 125 000 |
| Provision for depreciation | 37 500 |
| Provision for doubtful debts | 370 |
| Rent received in advance | 770 |

b. Prepare a statement of financial position (balance sheet) at 31 July 2018.

**Guidance**

In the current asset section provide details of accounts receivable, the provision for doubtful debts and the net figure.

**18. Income statement (profit and loss section) and statement of financial position (balance sheet) including adjustments, bad debts, provisions for doubtful debts and depreciation**

a. State **one** factor that should be taken into account when deciding the annual depreciation charge on a non-current asset.

Kathy owns a wholesale business called "Superior Kitchen Supplies". On 30 June 2018 the trading section of the business's income statement had already been prepared for the year ended on that date. The following balances appear in the business's books of account on this date.

|  | Dr | Cr |
|---|---|---|
|  | $ | $ |
| Accounts payable |  | 23 380 |
| Accounts receivable | 17 400 |  |
| Administration expenses | 13 920 |  |
| Bad debts | 860 |  |
| Bank loan (repayable February 2019) |  | 6 000 |
| Bank loan interest | 400 |  |
| Buildings |  |  |
|    Cost | 185 000 |  |
|      Provision for depreciation |  | 14 800 |
| Capital |  | 192 100 |
| Cash at bank | 8 240 |  |
| Delivery vehicles |  |  |
|    Cost | 48 000 |  |
|      Provision for depreciation |  | 12 000 |
| Discounts | 590 | 780 |
| Drawings | 23 100 |  |
| Electricity charges | 5 520 |  |
| Gross profit |  | 137 300 |
| Inventory, 30 June 2018 | 33 850 |  |
| Provision for doubtful debts, 1 July 2017 |  | 930 |
| Repairs and maintenance | 4 480 |  |
| Rent received |  | 6 620 |
| Wages | 52 550 |  |
|  | 393 910 | 393 910 |

Additional information:

- Administration expenses of $560 had been paid in advance at 30 June 2018.
- Interest on the bank loan is charged at 8% per annum. No interest had been paid on the loan for the months of May and June 2018. The balance of the bank loan account had been $6 000 through the year ended 30 June 2018.
- Rent received includes $2 400 which represents rent for the quarter ended 31 July 2018.
- Kathy's policy is to depreciate buildings by 2% per annum on cost and delivery vehicles by 25% per annum using the reducing balance method.
- The provision for doubtful debts should be maintained at 5% of accounts receivable at 30 June 2018.

**b.** Prepare the profit and loss section of the income statement for the year ended 30 June 2018.

**c.** Prepare the statement of financial position (balance sheet) at 30 June 2018.

> **Guidance**
> There are some complicated adjustments to really test your skills in this question. It is very important to take your time over these calculations and to set out your workings in detail.

### 19. An income statement with adjustments including those for capital expenditure

Anika owns "Summertown Stores". The following details are available about her business's financial year ended 30 September 2018.

Trial balance (extract) at 30 September 2018

|  | Dr $ | Cr $ |
|---|---|---|
| Carriage inwards | 1 670 | |
| Electricity charges | 5 690 | |
| Equipment | | |
|     Cost | 49 500 | |
|     Provision for depreciation, 1 October 2017 | | 11 800 |
| Insurance | 3 440 | |
| Inventory, 1 October 2017 | 17 420 | |
| Office expenses | 5 510 | |
| Purchases | 272 300 | |
| Rent expense | 14 900 | |
| Returns | 3 880 | 4 250 |
| Revenue | | 403 200 |
| Wages and salaries | 51 300 | |

Additional information:

- On 14 October 2017 Anika purchased additional equipment for $18 000. She had to pay carriage charges for the delivery of the equipment of $500. The carriage charges had been debited to the carriage inwards account. Anika's policy is to provide a full year's depreciation of equipment on all equipment using a rate of 15%.
- Inventory was valued at $16 140 on 30 September 2018.
- Insurance $670 was prepaid at 30 September 2018.
- Rent of $3 600 for the quarter ended 30 November 2018 was due but unpaid at 30 September 2018.
- Anika has decided to create a provision for doubtful debts at 4% of accounts receivable which were $12 000 at 30 September 2018.
  - **a.** Calculate the total cost of equipment following the purchase of additional equipment on 14 October 2017.
  - **b.** Calculate the depreciation charge on equipment for the year ended 30 September 2018.
  - **c.** Prepare an income statement for the year ended 30 September 2018.

**Guidance**

This question tests your understanding that the value of a non-current asset can be made up of a number of different payments. It is important to establish the correct cost of non-current assets otherwise depreciation calculations will be incorrect.

20. **Financial statements including adjustments for a service business**

    Kadema owns "Premier Car Hire". His business's financial year ended on 31 October 2018 when the following trial balance was prepared.

| | Dr | Cr |
|---|---|---|
| | $ | $ |
| Accounts payable | | 880 |
| Accounts receivable | 4 800 | |
| Bad debt | 120 | |
| Capital | | 270 000 |
| Cash at bank | 7 890 | |
| Cash in hand | 320 | |
| Drawings | 31 330 | |
| Furniture and equipment | | |
| Cost | 6 300 | |
| Provision for depreciation | | 1 260 |
| Insurance | 8 320 | |
| Motor vehicle running costs | 11 490 | |
| Motor vehicles | | |
| Cost | 95 000 | |
| Provision for depreciation | | 19 000 |
| Motor vehicles repairs | 3 940 | |
| Office expenses | 840 | |
| Premises | | |
| Cost | 230 000 | |
| Provision for depreciation | | 6 900 |
| Provision for doubtful debts | | 210 |
| Rent receivable | | 1 850 |
| Revenue | | 125 610 |
| Wages and salaries | 25 360 | |
| | 455 710 | 455 710 |

The following additional information is available at 31 October 2018:

- Office expenses $140 was due but unpaid.
- Insurance includes $190 paid in advance.
- Rent $290 has been received in advance.
- The provision for doubtful debts is to be reduced to $140.
- Depreciation is to be provided on non-current assets as follows: premises $6 900; furniture and equipment 20% per annum on cost; motor vehicles 20% per annum using the reducing balance method.
  - a. Prepare an income statement for the year ended 31 October 2018.
  - b. Prepare a statement of financial position (balance sheet) at 31 October 2018.

## Guidance

As this is a service business the income statement is made up of revenue plus other income less expenses. There are no purchases or inventory figures to record.

## 💬 Introduction

In this chapter there are questions to test your understanding of control systems that are used to help ensure that accounting records are error free. You will answer questions on:
- the trial balance and error correction
- control accounts
- bank reconciliation.

## Paper 1 questions

1. Brandon entered the payment for property rent into the property repairs account in error. What type of error is this?

   **A** error of commission
   **B** error of omission
   **C** error of original entry
   **D** error of principle

2. Marva entered the payment for a new motor vehicle into the motor repairs account in error. What type of error is this?

   **A** error of commission
   **B** error of omission
   **C** error of original entry
   **D** error of principle

3. A cheque payment of $76 to an account payable was recorded in the cash book as $67. What type of error is this?

   **A** error of commission
   **B** error of complete reversal
   **C** error of omission
   **D** error of original entry

4. Henry has prepared his income statement for the year showing a net profit of $33 600. He has now discovered the following two errors:
   - An accrual for wages of $1 400 has been omitted.
   - A prepayment for rent has been understated by $500.

   What is the correct net profit for the year?
   **A** $31 700      **B** $32 700      **C** $34 500      **D** $35 500

5. Samara has prepared her income statement for the year showing a net profit of $58 100. She has now discovered the following two errors.
   - The depreciation charge for the year has been understated by $3 000.
   - Carriage inwards of $800 was incorrectly added to the gross profit.

What is the correct net profit for the year?

   **A** $53 500    **B** $54 300    **C** $55 900    **D** $56 700

6. What are the sources of information which are used when preparing control accounts?

   **A** books of original entry

   **B** invoices

   **C** ledger accounts

   **D** trial balances

7. Which of the following items should be entered on the credit side of an accounts receivable control account?

   **A** cash sales

   **B** discounts allowed

   **C** refunds to accounts receivable

   **D** purchases returns

8. An accounts payable control account contained the following items.

| | $ |
|---|---|
| Credit balance at beginning of period | 4 500 |
| Credit purchases | 5 900 |
| Interest charged on overdue accounts | 200 |
| Payments to accounts payable | 5 400 |

What was the closing balance of the accounts payable control account?

   **A** $3 800    **B** $4 200    **C** $4 800    **D** $5 200

9. Grant was preparing his business's bank reconciliation statement and he was aware of the following details.

- amounts not yet credited by the bank $1 900
- bank balance in the cash book, $6 700 debit
- unpresented cheques $2 300

What is the balance shown on the bank statement?

   **A** $2 500    **B** $6 300    **C** $7 100    **D** $10 900

10. The bank columns of a retailer's cash book showed a credit balance of $540. When the bank statement for the period was received it was necessary to make entries for the following items.

- bank charges $40
- credit transfers received $280
- standing order payments $80

What was the balance of the bank columns after updating the cash book?

   **A** $140 credit   **B** $380 credit   **C** $700 credit   **D** $940 credit

# Paper 2 questions: Correction of errors

## 11. Correcting errors not revealed by the trial balance

a. Explain **two** benefits of preparing a trial balance.

The following errors were made by an accounts clerk in the current financial year.

I. A cheque payment of $480 for a motor repair was posted to the debit of rent and rates account.

II. A cheque payment of $1 260 for insurance was completely overlooked.

III. A cheque receipt of $415 from Susan Ellis was credited to the account of Suzanne Ellis.

IV. A cheque payment of £1 450 for plant and machinery had been posted to the debit of repairs and maintenance.

V. A purchase invoice for $230 for stationery from Paper Supplies Ltd, a credit supplier, had been entered in the records as $320.

b. Identify the type of error in each of the above cases.

c. Prepare journal entries to correct each of the above errors.

### Guidance

None of the above errors affect the agreement of the trial balance totals, so a suspense account is not required. If you find you are not quite sure how the ledger accounts should be corrected, you may find it a good idea to quickly draft the accounts concerned and record the errors described. This may help you visualise the corrections that are required. Don't forget that a narrative is required for each journal entry (unless the question specifically states otherwise) and to name the type of error concerned as part of each narrative.

## 12. Correcting errors revealed by the trial balance

a. Explain briefly, the difference between:

i. an error of commission and an error of principle

ii. an error of omission and an error of original entry.

An accounts clerk was unable to get the totals of the trial balance to agree. The totals were Dr $38 850, Cr $39 050. A suspense account has been opened and debited with the difference. The following errors have now been discovered:

- The sales journal was overcast by $200.
- Interest received of £130 has been correctly entered in the cash book but has not been posted to the interest received account.
- A cash payment of $25 for postage has been correctly entered in the cash book but has not been posted to the postage account.
- A sales invoice for $105 to Dorsey Ltd, a credit customer had been correctly entered in the sales journal, but had not been posted to Dorsey Ltd's account in the sales ledger.

b. Prepare journal entries to correct these errors.

c. Prepare the suspense account.

## Guidance

All of these errors do affect the agreement of the trial balance totals. When you have prepared the journal entries to correct the errors, open the suspense account with the difference on the trial balance and enter the relevant parts of the journal to it. The suspense account should then balance as there are no errors left to correct and the totals of a redrafted trial balance would agree. Include a narrative with each journal entry.

13. **Correcting errors involving the suspense account where the difference in the trial balance totals is unknown.**

   a. Explain the purpose of a suspense account.

   The totals of a business's trial balance did not agree. Subsequently, the following errors were discovered.

   - A cheque payment of $440 for repairs was entered correctly in the cash book, but not posted to repairs account.
   - The sales journal was undercast by $100.
   - A cheque received of $290 from Ingrid, a credit customer, had been entered correctly in the cash book, but had not been posted to Ingrid's account.

   b. Prepare journal entries to correct these errors.
   c. Prepare the suspense account and identify the original difference in the trial balance totals.

## Guidance

All of the above errors affect the balancing of the trial balance. After preparing the journal entries, post the necessary entries to a suspense account and the balance on this account will be the original difference in the trial balance totals. Remember the word "undercast" means to calculate a total which is less than it should be; and "overcast" means to calculate a total which is more than it should be.

14. **Correcting errors, some of which affect the suspense account.**

   a. Explain why it is necessary to double the amount of the error when correcting an error of complete reversal.

   An accounts clerk was unable to get the totals of the trial balance to agree. The totals were Dr $46 020, Cr $46 240. The following errors have now been discovered:

   - A sales invoice for $360 for Clifton, had been incorrectly posted to the sales ledger account of Cleavon.
   - The total of the discounts received column in the cash book had been overcast by $200.
   - A receipt of $120 for interest received had been posted to the debit of interest received account and the credit of bank account.
   - A cheque payment of $180 for motor repairs had been correctly entered in the cash book but had been posted to the motor repairs account as $160.

   b. Prepare journal entries to correct the errors. (Narratives are **not** required.)
   c. Prepare the suspense account.

15. **Correcting a draft net profit figure**

    a. Give **one** example of an error which can be ignored when correcting a draft net profit figure.

       Sara has prepared her income statement for the year ended 31 August 2018. The income statement showed a net profit of $38 300. The following errors have now been discovered:
       - Rent of $2 500 had been prepaid but no adjustment had been made.
       - Revenue had been overstated by $1 900.
       - Depreciation of $4 800 had been completely omitted from the income statement.
       - Advertising costs owing of $300 were overlooked when preparing the income statement.

    b. Prepare a statement showing the effect of correcting these errors on the profit for the year.

16. **Correcting a draft net loss figure**

    a. Name **one** type of error which would **not** be revealed by a trial balance. Give **one** example of this type of error.

       Erik has prepared his income statement for the year ended 31 July 2018. The income statement shows a net loss of $2 700. Erik has now discovered the following errors:
       - Discount received of $700 had been incorrectly deducted from the gross profit.
       - The accrual for heat and light had been overstated by $500.
       - Cash sales of $13 600 had been completely omitted from the accounting records.
       - An accrual for bank interest paid of $800 had been overlooked.
       - The prepayment for rent had been understated by $4 500.

    b. Prepare a statement showing the effect of correcting these errors on the net loss for the year.

# Paper 2 questions: Bank reconciliation

17. **Comparing a cash book and bank statement, updating the cash book and preparing a bank reconciliation statement**

   a. Explain the difference between a direct debit and a standing order.

   On 31 May 2018 the following bank statement was received by the accounts department of Raslinda Enterprises.

Premier Bank plc

Bank Statement for Raslinda Enterprises

| Date | | Details | Dr | Cr | Balance | |
|---|---|---|---|---|---|---|
| May | 1 | Balance | | | 4 880 | Cr |
| | 3 | Sundry credit | | 850 | 5 730 | Cr |
| | 8 | 723556 TDP Ltd | 475 | | 5 255 | Cr |
| | 11 | Credit transfer C Thomas | | 390 | 5 645 | Cr |
| | 14 | DD Regional Telecoms | 220 | | 5 425 | Cr |
| | 18 | 723558 Hatford Ltd | 188 | | 5 237 | Cr |
| | 20 | Charges | 54 | | 5 183 | Cr |
| | 25 | 723560 D Castle | 293 | | 4 890 | Cr |
| | 26 | Sundry credit | | 1 370 | 6 260 | Cr |

The business's cash book (bank columns) for May 2018 was as follows.

| Dr | | | Cash Book (bank columns only) | | | | Cr |
|---|---|---|---|---|---|---|---|
| May | 1 | Balance | 4 880 | May | 2 | TDP Ltd (chq 723556) | 475 |
| | 2 | Cash sales | 850 | | 4 | T Rajiv (chq 723557) | 833 |
| | 23 | L Pulchan | 820 | | 8 | Hatford Ltd (chq 723558) | 188 |
| | 23 | M Marco | 550 | | 19 | Metro plc (chq 723559) | 1 380 |
| | 29 | Cash sales | 1 230 | | 22 | D Castle (chq 723560) | 293 |
| | | | | | 31 | Balance c/d | 5 161 |
| | | | 8 330 | | | | 8 330 |
| June | 1 | Balance b/d | 5 161 | | | | |

   b. Compare the cash book and bank statement for May 2018.
   c. Update the cash book at 31 May 2018.
   d. Prepare a bank reconciliation statement dated 31 May 2018.

## Guidance

Task **b.** – when making the comparison it is a good idea to tick the items which appear in both documents as this helps isolate those items which will be required when answering tasks **b.** and **c**. Task **c.** – remember you are adding items to the cash book which are currently only shown in the bank statement. Task **d.** – the reconciliation statement makes use of those items currently shown in the cash book but missing from the bank statement.

18. **Updating the cash book and preparing a bank reconciliation statement working from a list of items including errors in the cash book or bank statement**

   a. Explain **two** benefits to the owner of a business in preparing bank reconciliation statements on a regular basis.

   On 31 August 2018 Shanise compared her cash book (bank columns) and bank statement for the August. On this date her cash book showed a debit balance of $2 382 and the bank statement showed a balance of $1 268 credit. Shanise has identified the following differences between the two records:
   - Bank charges of $84 which had been omitted from the cash book.
   - A cheque sent to a supplier, MBM Ltd, $332 had not been presented for payment.
   - A standing order for rent $485 had not been recorded in the cash book.
   - The bank had not yet recorded cash sales of $1 432 paid in on 29 August.
   - The bank statement included a credit transfer of $441 from a customer, G Parsons, which had not been recorded in the cash book.
   - A cheque for drawings $186 had been correctly recorded in the bank statement, but appears as $168 in the cash book.
   - There was an error in the bank statement: some interest on Shanise's investments $132 had been credited to Shanise's business account rather than her personal account.

   b. Update the cash book at 31 August 2018.
   c. Prepare a bank reconciliation statement at 31 August 2018.

> **Guidance**
>
> Don't forget to bring down the updated balance on the cash book and to give a full heading to the reconciliation statement which includes the date.

19. **Working with a bank overdraft**

   Rockfort Stores is a retail business. The following cash book (bank columns) was prepared during the month of January 2018.

| Dr | | | Cash Book (bank columns only) | | | | Cr |
|---|---|---|---|---|---|---|---|
| Jan | 1 | Balance | 856 | Jan | 4 | SO insurance | 335 |
| | 10 | Abbey Ltd | 472 | | 8 | Tilt Ltd (chq 837441) | 1 578 |
| | 11 | Mungroo Ltd | 314 | | 11 | Lisa Jones (chq 837442) | 896 |
| | 23 | Cash sales | 471 | | 15 | DD water charges | 540 |
| | 30 | Cash sales | 573 | | 21 | Hedrix plc (chq 837443) | 1 397 |
| | 31 | Balance c/d | 2 360 | | 26 | Cash (chq 837444) | 300 |
| | | | 5 046 | | | | 5 046 |
| | | | | Feb | 1 | Balance b/d | 2 360 |

   The business's bank statement for January 2018 was as follows.

Southern National Bank plc
Bank Statement for Rockfort Stores

| Date | | Details | Dr | Cr | Balance | |
|---|---|---|---|---|---|---|
| Jan | 1 | Balance | | | 856 | Cr |
| | 4 | SO Topmarks Insurance plc | 335 | | 521 | Cr |

| | | | | | |
|---|---|---|---|---|---|
| 11 | Chq 837441 Tilt Ltd | 1578 | | 1057 | Dr |
| 15 | Sundry credit | | 786 | 271 | Dr |
| 15 | DD Crystal Water Co Ltd | 540 | | 811 | Dr |
| 17 | Credit Transfer Helt plc | | 480 | 331 | Dr |
| 26 | Charges | 139 | | 470 | Dr |
| 27 | Chq 837442 Lisa Jones | 896 | | 1366 | Dr |
| 28 | Sundry credit | | 471 | 895 | Dr |

a. Explain why the standing order payment for insurance on 4 January is shown as a credit entry in the cash book but appears as a debit entry in the bank statement.

It has been noticed that an error was made in the cash book. The entry for cash sales on 30 January for $573 should have been for $375.

b. Taking account of all the available information, update the bank columns of the cash book on 31 January 2018.

c. What amount should be shown for the bank balance on Rockfort Stores' statement of financial position (balance sheet) at 31 January 2018? State whether this amount should be shown as a current asset or a current liability.

d. Prepare a bank reconciliation statement dated 31 January 2018.

---

**Guidance**

It is important to identify negative figures clearly in the reconciliation statement. The best way of doing this is to use brackets, for example, rather than writing −320, write (320).

---

## Paper 2 questions: Control accounts

### 20. Preparing control accounts for the sales ledger and the purchases ledger

a. Describe **two** benefits of preparing control accounts.

Henry regularly checks the accuracy of his business's sales and purchases ledger by preparing control accounts.

On 1 July 2018 the balances brought down on the two control accounts were:

| | $ |
|---|---|
| Accounts payable control account | 8920 |
| Accounts receivable control account | 11430 |

On 31 July 2018 the following totals were extracted from the books of original entry.

| | $ |
|---|---|
| Cash book: discounts allowed | 880 |
| Cash book: discounts received | 472 |
| Cash book: payments to accounts payable | 14950 |
| Cash book: receipts from accounts receivable | 22748 |
| Purchases book | 16327 |
| Purchases returns book | 589 |
| Sales book | 20445 |
| Sales returns book | 491 |

**b.** Prepare an accounts payable control account for July 2018.

**c.** Prepare an accounts receivable control account for July 2018.

## Guidance

Before you prepare your answer, identify items which are relevant to accounts payable for task **b.**, and those which are relevant to accounts receivable for task **c.** When deciding where to make entries it is helpful to remember: an accounts payable control account resembles an accounts payable account (so debit side for items which reduce the balance of the account and credit side for items which increase the balance of the account); an accounts receivable control account resembles an accounts receivable account (so debit side for items which increase the balance of the account and credit side for items which decrease the balance of the account).

21. **Preparing an accounts receivable control account with more unusual entries and selecting relevant details**

Nicole works in the accounts department of Horford Ltd. One of her duties is to prepare an accounts receivable control account at the end of each month.

On 1 February 2018 the balances brought down on the accounts receivable control account were: debit $23 786; credit $1 034.

The following information for February 2018 has been extracted from the company's books of account.

| | $ |
|---|---|
| Bad debts written off | 2 824 |
| Cash sales | 33 448 |
| Cheques received from accounts receivable but returned by the bank dishonoured | 827 |
| Contra entry (sales ledger account balances transferred to the purchases ledger) | 440 |
| Credit sales | 85 492 |
| Discounts allowed | 3 721 |
| Discounts received | 2 240 |
| Interest charged on overdue accounts of accounts receivable | 256 |
| Purchases returns | 4 483 |
| Receipts from accounts receivable (including dishonoured cheques) | 82 142 |
| Refunds to accounts receivable who overpaid their accounts | 163 |
| Sales returns | 3 462 |

On 28 February 2018 there were credit balances totalling $620 in the sales ledger.

**a.** State where Nicole will have obtained the information listed in the table above.

**b.** Prepare an accounts receivable control account for February 2018 selecting relevant details from the available information.

## Guidance

In this question there are some details which are not relevant to an accounts receivable control account, so they must be ignored. Only items which would appear in an individual receivable's account can also appear in an accounts receivable control account.

**22. Preparing accounts payable and accounts receivable control accounts including contra entries**

**a.** Explain why it is sometimes necessary to make a contra entry between a purchases ledger account and a sales ledger account.

Jason makes use of control accounts to check the accuracy of his business's purchases and sales ledger.

On 1 June 2018 the balances brought down on the accounts payable control account were: debit $414; credit $8 450.

Jason has provided the following information for June 2018.

| | $ |
|---|---:|
| Contra entry (purchases ledger balance transferred to the sales ledger) | 620 |
| Credit purchases | 23 726 |
| Credit sales | 40 185 |
| Discounts allowed | 382 |
| Discounts received | 561 |
| Payments to accounts payable | 24 372 |
| Purchases returns | 1 927 |
| Receipts from accounts receivable | 38 993 |
| Sales returns | 2 182 |

On 30 June 2018 there was a debit balance in the purchases ledger of $225.

**b.** Prepare an accounts payable control account for February 2018.

The total of credit balances in the purchases ledger on 28 February 2018 was $4 226.

**c.** Explain what conclusions can be drawn from this information.

**d.** Copy and complete the following table indicating whether each of the following items should be shown in the accounts receivable control account as a debit or credit entry. If the item should not be shown in the accounts receivable control accounts write "no entry".

| Item | Entry to be made in Sales Ledger Control Account |
|---|---|
| Credit sales | |
| Discounts allowed | |
| Purchases returns | |
| Contra entry (purchases ledger account balances transferred to the sales ledger) | |

**Guidance**

In task **c.** you should explain what it means if a control account closing balance does not agree with the figure for total receivables provided by the person responsible for preparing the sales ledger.

## Paper 1 questions

1. Which of the following should be entered in the appropriation account of a partnership?

|   | Interest on drawings | Interest on partners' capital | Drawings |
|---|---|---|---|
| A | ✓ | | ✓ |
| B | ✓ | ✓ | |
| C | | ✓ | ✓ |
| D | | ✓ | ✓ |

2. Which of the following should be entered on the credit side of a partner's current account?

|   | Interest on drawings | Interest on partners' capital | Share of residual profit |
|---|---|---|---|
| A | ✓ | | ✓ |
| B | ✓ | ✓ | |
| C | | ✓ | ✓ |
| D | ✓ | ✓ | |

3. Patsy and Romon are in partnership sharing profits and losses in the ratio 4:3 respectively. The partnership has just made a profit of $105 000. What entry should be made in Romon's current account?

   A  Credit $45 000

   B  Credit $60 000

   C  Debit $45 000

   D  Debit $60 000

4. Which of the following should be credited to a partner's current account?

   A  Drawings

   B  Interest on capital

   C  Interest on drawings

   D  Share of loss

5. Sharon and Trenton are in partnership sharing profits and losses equally. The partnership agreement provides for Trenton to receive a partnership salary of $10 000 per annum. The partnership made a net loss before appropriation of $32 000 during the year ended 31 December 2018.

What is Trenton's net share of the loss for the year ended 31 December 2018?

**A** $6 000     **B** $11 000     **C** $16 000     **D** $21 000

6. Rachel and Seema are in partnership sharing profits and losses equally after charging interest on drawings. During the year ended 30 September 2018, the partnership made a net profit before appropriation of $80 000. Interest on drawings for the year ended 30 September 2018 was: Rachel $5 000, Seema $3 000.

   What was Rachel's net share of the profits for the year?

   **A** $31 000     **B** $39 000     **C** $41 000     **D** $49 000

## Paper 2 questions

7. **Preparing an appropriation account including interest on capital and a partnership salary**

   Elizabeth and Marcus were considering forming a partnership. They realised that they would have more capital available as a result of forming the partnership, but that they would have unlimited liability for the debts of the business.

   **a.** State **two** other advantages that may arise from forming the partnership.

   **b.** State **one** other disadvantage that may arise from forming the partnership.

   When Elizabeth and Marcus formed their partnership they agreed to share profits and loses in the ratio 3:2. Their partnership agreement also includes the following:

   - The partners are to make capital contributions which are fixed at: Elizabeth $80 000; Marcus $50 000.
   - Elizabeth is to receive a partnership salary of $8 000 per annum.
   - Partners are entitled to interest on capitals at 8% per annum.

   During the year ended 30 November 2018, the partnership made a profit of $74 000.

   **c.** Prepare an appropriation account for the year ended 30 November 2018.

   > **Guidance**
   > Calculate each partner's interest on capital first and include your workings as part of your answer. Give the appropriation account a full title. Remember to start with the total profit and deduct each of the appropriations from this amount.

8. **Preparing partners' current accounts**

   **a.** Explain why you would advise partners to prepare a deed of partnership.

   Rhashan and Vishon are in partnership sharing profits and losses equally. On 1 January 2018 the balances of their current accounts were:

   Rashan     $4 500 debit

   Vishon     $6 200 credit

   The partnership made a profit of $38 600 during the year ended 31 December 2018. This was shared in accordance with the partnership agreement as follows.

- Interest on drawings: Rashan $640; Vishon $820.
- Partnership salary of $18 000 for Rashan.
- Interest on capital: Rashan $8 200; Vishon $7 400.

During the year ended 31 December 2018 the partners' drawings were: Rashan $16 000; Vishon $20 500.

**b.** Calculate each partner's share of the residual profit.

**c.** Prepare the partners' current accounts. Balance the accounts at 31 December 2018.

**d.** State what the closing balance of each partner's current represents.

## Guidance

It is a good idea to prepare one current account with separate columns for each partner as this saves time. Don't forget to bring down the closing balances on the partners' current accounts. Balances must always have a correct narrative, i.e. balance b/d, balance c/d. As task **c.** requires accounts, it would not be acceptable to present a calculation or vertical list of entries which contain a mix of positive and negative items.

9. **Preparing fluctuating capital accounts**

**a.** State the correct double entry required to record interest on a partner's loan.

André, Beverly and Calvin are in partnership sharing profits and losses in the ratio 4:3:3. The partners do not maintain separate capital and current accounts. Their partnership agreement provides that Beverly should receive a partnership salary of $10 000 per annum and Calvin should receive a partnership salary of $8 000 per annum. During the year ended 31 December the partnership made a small net profit of $11 000.
The following additional information is available:

| | André | Beverly | Calvin |
|---|---|---|---|
| | $ | $ | $ |
| Capital account balances, 1 January 2018 | 82 500 | 73 100 | 55 300 |
| Drawings during the year ended 31 December 2018 | 21 200 | 19 900 | 18 400 |

**b.** Prepare the partner's capital accounts for the year ended 31 December 2018.

10. **Preparing a partnership's statement of financial position (balance sheet)**

**a.** Describe **two** key features of a limited partnership.

Anika and Shauna are in partnership sharing profits and losses equally after allowing interest on the partners' fixed capitals at the rate of 10% per annum.
At 31 December 2018, the following balances appeared in the books of the partnership before the appropriation of profits for the year ended on that date and the preparation of a statement of financial position (balance sheet) at 31 December 2018.

|                                           | $       |        |
|-------------------------------------------|---------|--------|
| Accounts payable                          | 6 500   |        |
| Accounts receivable                       | 8 300   |        |
| Accruals                                  | 600     |        |
| Capital accounts                          |         |        |
|     Anika             | 60 000  |        |
|     Shauna            | 50 000  |        |
| Cash at bank                              | 3 200   |        |
| Current accounts, 1 January 2018          |         |        |
|     Anika             | 600     | debit  |
|     Shauna            | 2 500   | credit |
| Drawings                                  |         |        |
|     Anika             | 21 200  |        |
|     Shauna            | 26 500  |        |
| Inventory                                 | 14 200  |        |
| Non-current assets at net book value      | 87 300  |        |
| Prepayments                               | 700     |        |
| Profit for the year                       | 42 400  |        |

  **b.**  Calculate each partner's share of the profit for the year ended 31 December 2018.

  **c.**  Prepare the partnership's statement of financial position (balance sheet) at 31 December 2018. The statement should include detailed current accounts.

### Guidance

Provide detailed workings of each partner's profit share, as this information will be required when setting out the current accounts within the statement of financial position (balance sheet). Ensure that capital account and current account information is kept quite separate within the statement of financial position (balance sheet). It might be a good idea to show any negative figures in brackets, rather than use a minus sign; this form of presentation is likely to be much clearer.

11. **Sole traders form a partnership**

Grace and Kenton have each been in business as a sole traders for a number of years. They have now agreed to form a partnership that will start trading on 1 January 2019, and that all the assets and liabilities of each business will be transferred to the partnership.

  **a.**  State how profits and losses should be shared in their partnership if Grace and Kenton do not make any formal agreement.

The statements of financial position (balance sheets) of each business are shown below.

Grace

Statement of financial position

(balance sheet) at 31 December 2018

| | $ |
|---|---|
| Motor vehicles | 29 400 |
| Inventory | 11 900 |
| Accounts receivable | 4 800 |
| Cash at bank | 3 900 |
| | 50 000 |
| Capital | 35 400 |
| Bank loan | 8 000 |
| Accounts payable | 6 600 |
| | 50 000 |

Kenton

Statement of financial position

(balance sheet) at 31 December 2018

| | $ |
|---|---|
| Furniture and equipment | 18 300 |
| Inventory | 7 400 |
| Accounts receivable | 5 900 |
| | 31 600 |
| Capital | 19 800 |
| Accounts payable | 6 300 |
| Bank overdraft | 5 500 |
| | 31 600 |

b. Prepare a journal entry in the books of the new partnership to record Grace's contribution to the partnership on 1 January 2019.

c. Prepare the opening statement of financial position (balance sheet) of the new partnership on 1 January 2019.

## Guidance

In task **b.** remember a journal entry should have separate money columns labelled debit and credit, that accounts to be debited should be recorded first followed by accounts to be credited and that a narrative is required (unless a question makes it clear that this is not wanted). In task **c.** set out a formal statement of financial position (balance sheet) with a correct title, appropriate subheadings and just one bank account for the new business.

12. **Preparing a partnership's income statement and appropriation account including interest on a partner's loan and a more complex profit-sharing agreement**

One of the disadvantages of a partnership is that the partners do not enjoy "limited liability".

**a.** Explain what is meant by this disadvantage.

Kathy and Steve are in partnership sharing profits and losses equally. Their partnership agreement includes the following terms:

- Steve is entitled to receive interest on his loan at 5% per annum.
- Interest on total drawings should be charged at 10%.
- Each partner should receive interest on fixed capitals at 8% per annum.
- Kathy should receive an annual salary of $15 000.

The following information has been extracted from the partnership's books of account for the year ended 30 September 2018.

|  | $ |
|---|---|
| Administration expenses | 3 640 |
| Capital accounts | |
| Kathy | 90 000 |
| Steve | 70 000 |
| Carriage outwards | 1 430 |
| Drawings | |
| Kathy | 23 200 |
| Steve | 17 800 |
| Furniture and equipment | |
| At cost | 50 000 |
| Provision for depreciation, 1 October 2017 | 18 000 |
| Insurance | 3 410 |
| Inventory, 1 October 2017 | 14 440 |
| Loan from Steve | 18 000 |
| Purchases | 83 450 |
| Revenue | 139 910 |
| Sales returns | 830 |
| Wages | 29 620 |

Additional information:

- Inventory at 30 September 2018 was valued at $11 250.
- Insurance, $290, was prepaid at 30 September 2018.
- Wages due but unpaid totalled $430 at 30 September 2018.
- Depreciation should be provided on furniture and equipment at the rate of 20% per annum using the reducing-balance method.

**b.** Prepare an income statement for the year ended 30 September 2018.

**c.** Prepare an appropriation account for the year ended 30 September 2018.

## Guidance

Do not forget to present the financial statements with full titles and to show workings for adjustments and other calculations.

## Introduction

In this chapter there are questions to test your understanding of:
- the essential features of limited liability companies, co-operatives and non-profit making organisations
- methods of raising finance in a limited liability company
- types of share
- journal entries to record the issue of shares and debentures
- calculation of dividend payments
- appropriation of profits in a limited company
- preparing final accounts of limited companies and cooperatives
- analysing performance and position using ratios
- preparing receipts and payments accounts for non-profit organisations.

## Paper 1 questions

1. The directors of a company paid dividends on ordinary shares. In which of the company's financial statements will this be shown?

|   | Income statement | Appropriation account | Statement of financial position (balance sheet) |
|---|---|---|---|
| A | No | No | Yes |
| B | Yes | Yes | Yes |
| C | No | Yes | No |
| D | Yes | No | No |

2. Which of the following does **not** appear in the appropriation account of a limited company?

   A   debenture interest
   B   dividends paid
   C   dividends proposed
   D   transfers to reserves

3. Which of the following form part of the capital of a limited company?

   I.    debentures
   II.   ordinary shares
   iii.  preference shares

   A   I and II only
   B   I and III only
   C   II and III only
   D   I, II and III

**4.** A limited company has an authorised share capital of 500 000 ordinary shares of $0.50 each. The company's issued share capital is 400 000 ordinary shares. The directors paid a 10% dividend during the current financial year.

How much was the total dividend?

**A** $20 000    **B** $25 000    **C** $40 000    **D** $50 000

**5.** Which of the following should appear in the income statement of a limited company?

**I.** auditors' fees
**II.** debenture interest
**III.** directors' remuneration

   **A** I and II only
   **B** I and III only
   **C** II and III only
   **D** I, II and III

**6.** Which of the following are principles of co-operative societies?

**I.** democratic control
**II.** limited dividends on shares
**III.** restricted membership

   **A** I and II only
   **B** I and III only
   **C** II and III only
   **D** I, II and III

**7.** Which of the following is **not** a source of finance for a co-operative society?

**A** affiliation fees
**B** debentures
**C** donations
**D** grants

**8.** Which of the following should be included in the appropriation account of a co-operative society?

**A** auditors' remuneration
**B** donations
**C** honorarium
**D** membership fees

**9.** Which of the following should be included in the receipts and payments account of a sports club?

**I.** loans from members
**II.** members' subscriptions
**III.** purchase of sports equipment

   **A** I and II only
   **B** I and III only
   **C** II and III only
   **D** I, II and III

10. A social club has 50 members. The annual membership subscription fee is $100 per member. During the year ended 31 December 2018, 4 members paid their outstanding subscription for 2017, 40 members paid their annual subscription on time and 8 members paid their subscription in advance for 2019.

How much was received in members' subscriptions during 2018?

A   $4000      B   $4400      C   $5000      D   $5200

# Paper 2 questions

11. **Limited companies: the issue of shares and dividend calculations**

   a.   State **two** benefits of operating as a limited company rather than as a partnership.

   DXT Ltd was formed with an authorised capital of 800000 ordinary shares of $1 each and 200000 6% preference shares of $2.50 each.

   On 1 January 2018 the company issued three-quarters of its ordinary shares and all of its preference shares. The share issues were fully subscribed and paid up.

   b.   Describe **three** ways in which ordinary shares differ from preference shares.

   c.   Prepare journal entries to record the issue of:

   **i.**   ordinary shares

   **ii.**   preference shares.

> ## Guidance
> It is important to check the face (par) value of shares. Most shares have a face value of $1, but this is not always the case.

12. **Limited companies: preparing an income statement and appropriation account**

   a.   Describe **two** ways in which ordinary shares differ from debentures.

   The following is a list of balances extracted from the books of PQT Ltd on 31 December 2018.

   |  | $ |
   |---|---|
   | 8% debentures | 300000 |
   | Administration expenses | 33100 |
   | Auditors' fees | 8800 |
   | Cost of sales | 492000 |
   | Debenture interest paid | 12000 |
   | Dividends paid | 45000 |
   | Directors' remuneration | 48700 |
   | Distribution and selling costs | 21200 |
   | Non-current assets |  |
   |     Cost | 380000 |
   |     Provision for depreciation at 1 January 2018 | 76000 |
   | Ordinary share capital, 250000 shares of $5 each | 900000 |
   | Retained earnings at 1 January 2018 | 48400 |
   | Revenue | 850000 |

Additional information:

- Debenture interest for the second half of 2018 is outstanding.
- Distribution costs, $700, were paid in advance at 31 December 2018.
- Depreciation is provided on non-current assets at 20% per annum using the reducing balance method.
- The directors propose to transfer $75 000 to a general reserve.
- An ordinary dividend of 5% is proposed at 31 December 2018.

**b.** Prepare an income statement for the year ended 31 December 2018.

**c.** Prepare an appropriation account for the year ended 31 December 2018.

---

### Guidance

Make sure the financial statements are given full titles without abbreviations, and where calculations are necessary you provide details in the form of workings. Check that you have used labels for gross profit, net profit.

---

13. **Limited companies: preparing an appropriation account and statement of financial position (balance sheet); analysing performance**

**a.** Define the term "authorised capital".

The following trial balance was extracted from the books of JLJ Ltd at the end of its financial year, 30 September 2018.

|  | $000 | $000 |
|---|---|---|
| 10% Debentures (2025) |  | 200 |
| Accounts payable |  | 23 |
| Accounts receivable | 78 |  |
| Cash at bank | 41 |  |
| Debenture interest due but unpaid |  | 10 |
| Dividends paid | 80 |  |
| General reserve |  | 154 |
| Inventory | 57 |  |
| Net profit for the year |  | 402 |
| Non-current assets |  |  |
|     Cost | 1 770 |  |
|     Provision for depreciation |  | 300 |
| Ordinary share capital: 400 000 shares of $2 each |  | 800 |
| Provision for doubtful debts |  | 7 |
| Rent prepaid | 5 |  |
| Retained earnings at 1 October 2017 |  | 135 |
|  | 2 031 | 2 031 |

Additional information:

The directors are proposing the transfer of $220 000 to the general reserve and a dividend of 20 cents per share.

**b.** Prepare an appropriation account for the year ended 30 September 2018.

c. Prepare a statement of financial position (balance sheet) at 30 September 2018.

d. Calculate the company's return on investment for the year ended 30 September 2018.

> **Guidance**
>
> There is a lot to do in this question, so it is sensible before answering to look through the list of items in the trial balance and note where they should appear. It would be easy to forget that the proposed dividends should appear in both financial statements. The return on investment percentage should be based on the equity of the company at the beginning of the year.

14. **Co-operative societies: preparing an income statement and appropriation account**

a. Identify **three** key principles of co-operative societies.

The following information is available for the Southern Shores Co-operative Society at 31 December 2018.

|  | $ |
|---|---:|
| Administration costs | 5 980 |
| Annual general meeting costs | 2 240 |
| Auditors' remuneration | 4 190 |
| Dividends paid | 15 500 |
| Furniture and equipment at net book value | 27 600 |
| Insurance | 1 920 |
| Interest received on investments in other co-operatives | 5 850 |
| Membership fees | 42 300 |
| Premises | |
|     Cost | 125 000 |
|     Provision for depreciation at 1 January 2018 | 10 000 |
| Secretary's honorarium | 5 300 |
| Undistributed surplus at 1 January 2018 | 38 900 |

Additional information at 31 December 2018:

- Membership fees due but not yet received, $5 300.
- Insurance paid in advance, $280.
- Depreciation charges:
  - furniture and equipment: 15% per annum using the reducing balance method
  - premises: 4% per annum using the straight-line method
  - The board of management have agreed to transfer 30% of the surplus for the year to the statutory reserve.

b. Prepare an income and expenditure account for the year ended 31 December 2018.

c. Prepare an appropriation account for the year ended 31 December 2018.

> **Guidance**
>
> A common mistake is to treat an honorarium as an expense rather than an appropriation of the surplus. Don't forget that a co-operative society makes a surplus (rather than a net profit) or a deficit (rather than a net loss).

## 15. Co-operative societies: preparing an appropriation account and statement of financial position (balance sheet)

a. Define the term "honorarium".

The following balances appeared in the books of the Coral Seas Co-operative Society at 30 June 2018.

|  | $ | $ |
|---|---|---|
| Accounts payable | | 13 500 |
| Administration costs due but unpaid | | 700 |
| Cash at bank | 18 500 | |
| Dividends paid | 35 000 | |
| Honorarium | 12 600 | |
| Investments in other co-operative societies | 42 000 | |
| Membership fees received in advance | | 2 300 |
| Non-current assets | | |
| Cost | 580 000 | |
| Provision for depreciation | | 105 000 |
| Share capital (shares of $1 each) | | 370 000 |
| Statutory reserve | | 62 000 |
| Surplus for year | | 95 000 |
| Undistributed surplus at 1 July 2017 | | 39 600 |
| | 688 100 | 688 100 |

Note: 20% of the surplus for the year should be transferred to the statutory reserve.

b. Prepare an appropriation account for the year ended 30 June 2018.
c. Prepare a statement of financial position (balance sheet) at 30 June 2018.

### Guidance
In task c. remember that a co-operative society is financed from shares, statutory reserves and undistributed surpluses.

## 16. Non-profit organisations: receipts and payments accounts

a. Explain how a receipts and payments account will be useful to a club's committee.

The Southern Hills Sports Club was formed several years ago. The following information is available for the year ended 31 October 2018.

At 1 November 2017 the treasurer reports the club had the following cash resources:

|  | $ |
|---|---|
| Cash in hand | 370 |
| Cash at bank | 5 960 |

During the year ended 31 October 2018 the following amounts were received or paid.

|  | $ |
|---|---|
| Clubhouse and sports ground rent | 26 800 |
| Donations from local businesses | 16 300 |
| Members' subscriptions | See below |
| Office expenses | 2 750 |
| Proceeds from sales of old equipment | 520 |
| Purchases of new sports equipment | 8 900 |
| Refreshment purchases | 14 300 |
| Sales of refreshments | 22 980 |
| Sports competition prizes | 2 210 |
| Sports ground maintenance | 11 680 |
| Travel costs for away fixtures | 6 980 |
| Wages of refreshment staff | 7 260 |

The club has 180 members each of whom paid their annual subscription of $175. In addition, 22 members paid a subscription for the year ending 31 October 2019 in advance.

**b.** Prepare a receipts and payments account for the year ended 31 October 2018.

---

### Guidance

All receipts and payments are entered in the account. Set out details of any calculations, for example the members' subscriptions. Set out the account with a full heading and remember to include a label for receipts and a label for payments.

**Manufacturing and inventory control**

> ## Introduction
>
> In this chapter there are questions to test your understanding of:
> - manufacturing accounts
> - costing principles
> - inventory control.

## Paper 1 questions

1.  Which one of the following factory costs is a direct cost?

    **A**  carriage inwards on raw materials

    **B**  machinery repairs

    **C**  storekeeper's wages

    **D**  rent

2.  Which one of the following factory costs will increase as production increases in the short term?

    **A**  depreciation of machinery

    **B**  electricity

    **C**  insurance

    **D**  supervisor's salary

3.  Which of the following costs is included in the calculation of prime cost?

    **I.**  purchases of raw materials

    **II.**  carriage inwards on raw materials

    **III.**  production worker's wages

    **A**  I and II only

    **B**  I and III only

    **C**  II and III only

    **D**  I, II and III

4.  The following information was recorded in a manufacturing account.

    |  | $000 |
    |---|---|
    | Prime cost | 700 |
    | Indirect costs | 40 |
    | Opening inventory of work in progress | 10 |
    | Closing inventory of work in progress | 20 |

    What is this business's cost of production?

    |  | $000 |
    |---|---|
    | **A** | 650 |
    | **B** | 670 |
    | **C** | 730 |
    | **D** | 750 |

**5.** The following is information for a manufacturing business:

| | $000 |
|---|---|
| Carriage inwards of finished goods | 10 |
| Cost of production | 920 |
| Closing inventory of finished goods | 200 |
| Opening inventory of finished goods | 150 |
| Purchases of finished goods | 180 |

What is the business's cost of sales?

|   | $000 |
|---|---|
| A | 1 040 |
| B | 1 060 |
| C | 1 140 |
| D | 1 160 |

**6.** Which of the following is a factory indirect cost?

A   carriage charges on raw materials
B   carriage outwards
C   machinery maintenance costs
D   wages of machine operatives

**7.** Which of the following will remain unchanged if production decreases?

A   carriage inwards on raw materials
B   electricity
C   factory manager's salary
D   wages of machine operatives

**8.** Which of the following factors could be used to apportion indirect factory overheads between cost centres?

I.   floor space
II.  cost of machinery
III. number of employees

A   I and II only
B   I and III only
C   II and III only
D   I, II and III

**9.** A business uses the FIFO method of inventory valuation. The following information is available about a particular product for September 2018.

| Opening inventory | 10 @ $10 each |
|---|---|
| Purchases on 10 September | 10 @ $11 each |
| Purchases on 20 September | 10 @ $12 each |
| Sales 15 September | 15 items |

What was the value of the inventory in the stockroom at the end of the month?

**A** $165 **B** $170 **C** $175 **D** $180

10. A business uses the LIFO method of inventory valuation. Its closing inventory using this method was $800. This figure would have been $900 had the FIFO method of inventory valuation been used.

What would the effect have been on the profit figure had the business used the FIFO method of inventory valuation?

|   | Gross profit | Net profit |
|---|---|---|
| A | Decrease $100 | No change |
| B | Decrease $100 | Decrease $100 |
| C | Increase $100 | No change |
| D | Increase $100 | Increase $100 |

## Paper 2 questions

11. **Preparing a manufacturing account and trading section of an income statement**

   a. Explain what is meant by the terms (i) direct cost and (ii) indirect cost when preparing the financial statements of a manufacturing concern?

   HH Manufacturers make fishing equipment. The following information is available for the year ended 31 December 2018.

|   | $ |
|---|---|
| Carriage inwards on raw materials | 860 |
| Depreciation of factory machinery | 8 350 |
| Direct wages | 49 580 |
| Factory electricity | 4 910 |
| Factory insurance | 6 670 |
| Indirect wages and salaries | 21 320 |
| Inventories at 1 January 2018 | |
|     Raw materials | 11 820 |
|     Finished goods | 8 400 |
|     Work in progress | 6 290 |
| Inventories at 31 December 2018 | |
|     Raw materials | 14 390 |
|     Finished goods | 7 920 |
|     Work in progress | 5 310 |
| Machinery repairs and maintenance | 1 830 |
| Purchases of raw materials | 44 320 |
| Revenue (sales of finished goods) | 283 640 |
| Sales returns | 920 |

Additional information:

Direct wages $2 800 was due but unpaid at 31 December 2018.

Factory insurance includes a premium of $1 800 for the three months ended 28 February 2019.

**b.** Prepare a manufacturing account for the year ended 31 December 2018.

**c.** Prepare the trading section of the income statement for the year ended 31 December 2018 to identify the gross profit for the year ended on that date.

### Guidance

Before preparing the accounts it can be useful to work through the information in the list deciding what is a direct cost, what is an indirect factory cost and what is required for the trading section of the income statement. When preparing the financial statements remember that only factory costs are shown in a manufacturing account and that the trading section of the income statement is concerned with finished goods only. Check that you have identified and labelled the figure for cost of raw materials consumed and prime cost. Take care with the adjustment for factory insurance: you will notice that it is not the full amount of $1 800 which is prepaid. Check also that you remembered to add the subtotal for indirect costs to the prime cost (it is a common error to deduct this figure).

12. **Preparing a manufacturing account, income statement and extract from the statement of financial position (balance sheet); calculating the cost of production per unit**

**a.** Define "prime cost".

KX Products Ltd are manufacturers. The following information is available for the year ended 31 October 2018.

| | $ |
|---|---|
| Carriage outwards | 1 110 |
| Direct wages | 112 300 |
| Factory insurance | 5 650 |
| Factory supervisor's salary | 24 320 |
| Furniture and equipment | |
| Cost | 18 500 |
| Provision for depreciation at 1 November 2017 | 4 000 |
| Inventories 1 November 2017 | |
| Raw materials | 14 840 |
| Work in progress | 1 890 |
| Finished goods | 13 300 |
| Inventories 30 September 2018 | |
| Raw materials | 15 090 |
| Work in progress | 1 370 |
| Finished goods | 12 260 |
| Machinery | |
| Cost | 85 000 |
| Provision for depreciation at 1 November 2017 | 34 000 |
| Maintenance and repairs | 23 800 |

| | |
|---|---:|
| Power charges | 9 260 |
| Purchases of raw materials | 92 660 |
| Purchases returns (raw materials) | 770 |
| Rent | 24 800 |
| Revenue | 463 820 |

Additional information:

- Maintenance and repairs should be divided 90% to the factory and 10% to the rest of the business.
- Power charges were in arrears, $850, at 31 October 2018.
- Rent $1 300 was paid in advance at 31 October 2018; rent is divided 60% to the factory and 40% to the rest of the business.
- Depreciation is to be charged on machinery at the rate of 20% on cost, and on furniture and equipment at the rate of 15% using the reducing balance method.

**b.** Prepare a manufacturing account for the year ended 31 October 2018.

**c.** Prepare an income statement for the year ended 31 October 2018.

**d.** Prepare an extract from the statement of financial position (balance sheet) at 31 October 2018 showing how inventories should be recorded.

During the year ended 31 October 2018 the company made 4 300 identical units.

**e.** Calculate the cost of producing one unit.

## Guidance

As always when preparing a manufacturing account remember to label subtotals and cost of production correctly. Particular care is required with the adjustment to rent: it is important to take account of the prepayment before dividing the expense between the factory and the rest of the business. When preparing the extract from the statement of financial position (balance sheet) it is important to show each individual inventory; it is a common mistake to show just one figure for total inventories.

## 13. Calculating the selling price of a product

**a.** In a manufacturing organisation what is meant by the term "work in progress"?

Miguel makes kayaks. During one month, Miguel aims to produce 30 kayaks.

The following direct costs are incurred when making one kayak.

| | $ |
|---|---|
| Direct materials | 3.5 kg at $14.50 per kg |
| Direct labour | 2.8 hrs at $12.20 per hour |

The business's indirect costs per month are as follows:

| | $ |
|---|---|
| Depreciation charges | 700 |
| Insurance | 360 |
| Power | 440 |

Miguel's policy is to calculate a selling price using a mark-up of 75% .

**b.** Calculate the cost of making one kayak.

**c.** Calculate the selling price of a kayak.

   Island Holidays Ltd has ordered 22 kayaks from Miguel.

**d.** Calculate the profit that should be made on this order.

> **Guidance**
> Provide workings for each direct cost and present the calculations in a table labelling each item.

## 14. Using absorption costing

In absorption costing some indirect costs are allocated and some indirect costs are apportioned.

**a.** Explain the difference between the terms "allocated" and "apportioned".

   MYQ Ltd is a manufacturing company. It has two production departments: cutting and finishing.

   The following costs are expected to arise in December 2018:

| | Cutting department | Finishing department |
|---|---|---|
| | $ | $ |
| Allocated indirect costs | 18 400 | 13 200 |

Indirect costs to be apportioned:

| | $ |
|---|---|
| Rent | 16 800 |
| Wages of department supervisors | 31 500 |

Additional information:

| | Cutting department | Finishing department |
|---|---|---|
| Floor space (sq m) | 32 | 8 |
| Number of employees | 11 | 4 |
| Machine hours available per month | 5 500 | 420 |
| Labour hours available per month | 4 400 | 640 |

**b.** Calculate a suitable overhead absorption rate for each department (to two decimal places).

   The company has received an order which will require the following:

| Direct materials | 14 kilograms at $5.30 per kilogram |
|---|---|
| Direct labour | 5 hours in the cutting department at $12.50 per hour |
| | 1.5 hours in the finishing department at $10.20 per hour |
| Machine hours | 6 hours in the cutting department |
| | 0.75 hours in the finishing department |

The company's policy is to mark-up the cost of all orders by 50%.

**c.** Calculate the selling price of the order.

## Guidance

In task **b.** it is recommended that your answer is set out as a table which has a column for listing the indirect costs and an additional two columns, one for each department; have separate rows for each indirect cost and state the basis for apportioning the rent and wages of department supervisors. The final row in the table will be used to total the indirect costs for each department. Under the table set out detailed calculations of the overhead absorption rates for each department choosing the dominant feature in each department (labour hours or machine hours) in each calculation. In task **c.** again set out a detailed calculation which lists direct materials, direct labour and then overhead costs for each department, making use of the overhead absorption rates calculated in task **b.**

### 15. Inventory controls

At 31 December 2018 three local retailers are preparing end of year financial statements and are about to value their closing inventories.

*Karine's general stores*

Karine uses the FIFO method of inventory valuation. The following details are available for 2018 for one particular unit which she retails.

- January: opening inventory 15 items @ $12 each
- March: received 10 items @ $13 each
- December: issued 12 items

**a.** Calculate the value of Karine's closing inventory of this item using the FIFO method.

*Lloyd's fishing supplies*

Lloyd uses the LIFO method of inventory valuation. The following details are available for 2018 for one particular unit which he retails.

- January: opening inventory 40 Items @ $32 each
- August: received 30 items @ $34 each
- December: issued 27 items

**b.** Calculate the value of Lloyd's closing inventory of this item using the LIFO method.

*Monica's furniture stores*

Monica uses the AVCO method of inventory valuation. The following details are available for 2018 for one particular unit which she retails.

- January: opening inventory 20 items @ $25
- July: received 40 items @ $30 each
- December: issued 28 items

**c.** Calculate the value of Monica's closing inventory after using the AVCO method.
**d.** If prices are rising which of the methods of inventory used by the three retailers will give the highest profit figure?

## Guidance

In **a.**, **b.** and **c.** provide detailed workings for your answers. It is recommended that your detailed workings show the value of the inventory after each receipt and each issue.

## Introduction

In this chapter there are questions to test your understanding of:

- methods of payment
- basic source documents for the payroll
- preparation of spreadsheets to arrive at net pay amounts
- main accounting software for payroll
- distinguishing between statutory and voluntary deductions
- calculating employees' earnings
- preparing cash flow projections for a six-month period
- preparing sales and production budgets for a three-month period
- preparing a simple business plan.

## PAPER 1 QUESTIONS

1. Which of the following is a voluntary deduction from an employee's pay?

   I. donation to a favourite charity

   II. membership of a trade union

   III. national insurance (social security) contribution

   A  I and II only

   B  I and III only

   C  II and III only

   D  I, II and III

2. Which of the following is a statutory deduction from an employee's pay?

   I. contribution to saving scheme

   II. income tax

   III. national insurance

   A  I and II only

   B  I and III only

   C  II and III only

   D  I, II and III

3. Which of the following is a source document for pay calculations?

   I. clock card

   II. piecework ticket

   III. time sheet

   A  I and II only

   B  I and III only

   C  II and III only

   D  I, II and III

**4.** George works a 40-hour week and is paid $30 per hour. Overtime is paid at time and a half. During a recent week George worked for 42 hours.

What was George's gross pay?

A $1 200     B $1 260     C $1 290     D $1 320

**5.** Sharla has been promoted and her monthly salary of $3 000 will increase by 10%. Sharla pays tax at the rate of 20% after deducting a monthly personal allowance of $1 000.

By how much will Sharla's take home pay increase after her promotion?

A $160     B $200     C $240     D $300

**6.** Renea is making a cash flow projection for her business for the next few months. She expects the business to have a bank overdraft of $2 000 at the beginning of the forecast period.

Her forecasts for the first two months are as follows:

|         | Inflows | Outflows |
|---------|---------|----------|
|         | $       | $        |
| Month 1 | 10 000  | 3 000    |
| Month 2 | 5 000   | 9 000    |

What is the business's forecast bank balance at the end of month 2?

A negative $5 000

B negative $1 000

C positive $5 000

D positive $1 000

**7.** Which of the following is **not** a cash inflow?

A cash sales

B credit sales

C grants

D receipts from customers

**8.** Which of the following is **not** a cash outflow?

A annual service of motor vehicle

B depreciation of motor vehicle

C fuel for motor vehicle

D purchase of motor vehicle

**9.** Cindy is preparing a production budget. Closing inventory is always based on 20% of the following month's sales. Units cost $1 each to produce.

The following is an extract from the business's sales budget:

|               | Month 1 | Month 2 | Month 3 |
|---------------|---------|---------|---------|
| Sales (units) | 100     | 120     | 140     |

What entry should be made in the production budget for production for Month 2?

A 124 units     B 148 units     C $124     D $148

10. Which of the following should be included in a business plan?

I. capital requirements

II. expected market trends

III. key personnel

    A   I and II only

    B   I and III only

    C   II and III only

    D   I, II and III

# PAPER 2 QUESTIONS

11. **Calculating gross pay using fixed rates, time rates and piece rates**

a.  Describe the information you would expect to find on an employee's payslip.

DKJ Ltd is a manufacturing business. The following details are available about three of the business's employees.
Mala is the sales manager. Her salary in 2017 was $87 000 per annum. In 2018 she was given a pay rise and her salary increased by 5% per annum.

b.  Calculate the increase in Mala's monthly gross salary comparing 2018 with 2017.

Zamran works in the maintenance department. He works a 40-hour week with overtime paid at time and a half. His rate of pay is $36 per hour.
During one week in 2018 Zamran worked for 43 hours.

c.  Calculate Zamran's gross wage for the week.

Bradley works in the production department where three products are made. The piece rates are as follows:

|  | $ per item |
|---|---|
| Jex | 4 |
| Kex | 7 |
| Lex | 8 |

During one week in 2018 Bradley completed the following items:

| Jex | 22 |
|---|---|
| Kex | 13 |
| Lex | 11 |

d.  Calculate Bradley's gross wage for the week.

> **Guidance**
> It is important to set out the details of each calculation.

12. **Calculating gross pay using piece rates with quality control, commission, etc.**

a.  State the information you would expect to extract from an employee's clock card when preparing the payroll.

WPY Ltd manufacturers computer components. Owen works in the production department and is paid a piece rate of $2.20 per item. His work record for Week 11 in 2018 was as follows:

|  | Complete items | Rejected items |
|---|---|---|
| Monday | 511 | 27 |
| Tuesday | 492 | 21 |
| Wednesday | 531 | 17 |
| Thursday | 502 | 19 |
| Friday | 479 | 15 |

**b.** Calculate Owen's gross wage for Week 11.

Sherry works in the company's sales department. She earns a monthly salary of $3 150. In addition she is entitled to receive a commission of 2% of the company's monthly sales which exceed the target of $320 000. In December 2018 the company's sales totalled $352 000.

**c.** Calculate Sherry's gross salary for December 2018.

## Guidance

In task **a.** provide as full an answer as you can. Set out detailed calculations in tasks **b.** and **c.**

## 13. Calculating net pay

**a.** Explain the difference between statutory and voluntary deductions from gross pay.

Laurelle and Nico work for Ace Sports, a wholesale business. Laurelle is the finance manager and earns a salary of $102 000 per annum. Nico works in the warehouse and is paid $32 per hour for a 40-hour week with overtime paid at time and a quarter.

The following information is available about deductions from gross pay.

| Income tax | Personal allowance: $18 000 per annum<br>Basic rate 20% |
|---|---|
| National insurance | 4% of gross pay |
| Pension scheme | 3% of gross pay |
| Trade union contributions | $12 per week |

Nico belongs to the trade union.

**b.** Calculate Laurelle's monthly net pay. Set out a detailed statement of gross pay and deductions.

**c.** Calculate Nico's net pay for a week in which he worked for 44 hours. Set out a detailed statement of gross pay and deductions.

## Guidance

In task **a.** it is a good idea to give an example of each type of deduction. This is because the task requires you to "explain". It is recommended you work to two decimal places where necessary in the calculations.

## 14. Preparing cash flow projections

Stephen is planning to open a business as an advertising agency.

**a.** Identify **four** main sections he should include in his business plan.

He has prepared the following forecast cash inflows and outflows for the business's first six months.

| | Month | | | | | |
|---|---|---|---|---|---|---|
| | 1 | 2 | 3 | 4 | 5 | 6 |
| | $ | $ | $ | $ | $ | $ |
| Capital introduced | 33 000 | | | | | |
| Sales revenue | 4 500 | 6 000 | 7 000 | 8 000 | 9 000 | 9 000 |
| Bank loan | | | | 5 000 | | |
| Purchase of non-current assets | 28 000 | | | 8 000 | | |
| Assistant's wages | 5 400 | 5 400 | 5 400 | 5 600 | 5 600 | 5 600 |
| Utility charges | 300 | 300 | 300 | 400 | 400 | 400 |
| Rent | 900 | 900 | 900 | 900 | 900 | 900 |

**b.** Prepare a cash flow projection for each of the business's first six months.

### Guidance

In task **b.** take your time to set up the table required for the cash flow projections. Label each entry carefully. It is recommended that the cash receipts are entered and totalled and the cash payments are entered and totalled before attempting to work out the balances at the beginning and end of each month.

## 15. Preparing cash flow projections and sales and production budgets

Dominique Ellis is planning to start a small manufacturing business called "Supreme Products". She is currently preparing a business plan.

**a.** Identify **four** examples of information she should include in the plan's executive summary.

She plans to sell 200 units in the business's first month, and then to increase sales by 10% each month compared to the previous month. Each unit will sell for $30.

**b.** Prepare a sales budget for each of the first three months.

In each month she will produce sufficient units to cover that month's forecast sales and to hold a closing inventory of 20% of the next month's sales. She expects sales in Month 4 to be 250 units.

**c.** Prepare a production budget for each of the first three months.

Dominique has been asked to prepare a cash flow projection for each of the business's first three months.

She has provided the following information:

- At the beginning of Month 1 she will invest $40 000 in the business.
- Each unit of production will cost $8 in materials and $12 in labour costs.
- She will purchase non-current assets of $32 000 at the beginning of Month 1.
- General expenses will be $1 200 per month which will be paid each month.
- Rent of the production area and offices will be $800 per month to be paid each month.

**d.** Prepare a cash flow projection for each of the business's first three months. Use information from the sales and production budgets as well as the details given above.

## Guidance

This is a more complex task requiring both budgets and a cash flow projection. Use the results of the sales budget and the production budget to make entries for cash sales and for payments for materials and for labour in the cash flow projection.

## Paper 1 questions

1. The owner of a business values inventory using the FIFO method every year and always depreciates non-current assets using the straight-line method to ensure each year's results can be compared on a valid basis.

   Which accounting concept is being applied by the owner of the business?

   A  accruals (matching)
   B  consistency
   C  prudence
   A  separate entity

2. Which of the following should follow the receipt of source documents in the accounting cycle?

   A  drawing up financial statements
   B  preparing ledger accounts
   C  preparing books of original entry
   A  using control systems

3. Which source document is used to make debit entries in the bank column of a cash book?

   A  a cheque counterfoil                      C  receipt
   B  paying-in slip counterfoil                D  till rolls

4. A bookkeeper is posting the totals of the sales returns book and the purchases book. Which of the following entries is correct?

   |   | Debit | Credit |
   |---|-------|--------|
   | A | Purchases<br>Sales returns | |
   | B | Purchases | Sales returns |
   | C | | Purchases<br>Sales returns |
   | D | Sales returns | Purchases |

5. Which of the following correctly lists how account balances should be recorded in a trial balance?

   |   | Debit | Credit |
   |---|-------|--------|
   | A | Bank overdraft<br>Discounts allowed | Discounts received<br>Sales |
   | B | Carriage inwards<br>Discounts received | Purchase returns<br>Bank overdraft |
   | C | Purchase returns<br>Carriage outwards | Discounts allowed<br>Sales |
   | D | Sales returns<br>Discounts allowed | Bank overdraft<br>Purchase returns |

6. The following balances were extracted from the books of a sole trader at the end of the business's financial year.

|  | $000 |
|---|---|
| Carriage inwards | 5 |
| Carriage outwards | 7 |
| Closing inventory less than opening inventory | 1 |
| Purchases | 80 |
| Purchase returns | 3 |
| Revenue | 120 |
| Sales returns | 4 |

What was the business's cost of sales?

A   $80 000      B   $81 000      C   $82 000      D   $84 000

7. At its financial year end a business had a working capital of $10 000 and current assets of $40 000 including inventory $5 000.

What was the business's acid test ratio?

A   1.17:1        B   1.33:1        C   3.50:1        D   4.00:1

8. Which of the following ratios shows how well a business has controlled its expenses?

A   current ratio
B   net profit as a percentage of revenue
C   rate of inventory turnover
D   return on investment

9. A business made a gross profit of $49 000 during a recent financial year. During the same period payments for expenses totalled $31 000 and receipts for other income totalled $8 000. At the year end expenses were prepaid $2 000 and other income in advance totalled $1 000. What was the business's net profit for the year?

A   $23 000      B   $25 000      C   $27 000      D   $29 000

10. A business has a provision for doubtful debts of $1 000. It has been decided to maintain the provision at 5% of accounts receivable which currently totals $18 000.

What entries will be required in the journal to update the provision for doubtful debts?

|  | Debit | Credit |
|---|---|---|
| A | Income statement $100 | Provision for doubtful debts $100 |
| B | Income statement $900 | Provision for doubtful debts $900 |
| C | Provision for doubtful debts $100 | Income statement $100 |
| D | Provision for doubtful debts $900 | Income statement $900 |

11. Which of the following is revenue expenditure for a manufacturer of sports equipment?

   I. carriage inwards on raw materials
   II. legal fees paid for purchase of factory buildings
   III. repairs to delivery vehicles

   A   I and II only
   B   I and III only
   C   II and III only
   D   I, II and III

12. Sophie's trial balance totals did not agree by $34 and this amount was debited to a suspense account. It has been discovered that the purchases account has been overcast by $34.

   Which entry should be made to correct this error?

|   | Debit | Credit |
|---|---|---|
| A | Accounts payable  $34 | Suspense $34 |
| B | Purchases $34 | Suspense $34 |
| C | Suspense $34 | Accounts payable $34 |
| D | Suspense $34 | Purchases $34 |

13. Carlos is reconciling his cash book balance with his bank statement balance. The following items have been found to account for the difference. Which of these items should be used to update the cash book.

   I. bank charges
   II. returned cheques
   III. unpresented cheques

   A   I and II only
   B   I and III only
   C   II and III only
   D   I, II and III

14. Which of the following items should appear on the credit side of an accounts payable control account?

   A   contra entries with sales ledger
   B   discounts received
   C   interest charged on overdue accounts
   D   purchase returns

15. Faye and Kerron are in partnership sharing profits and losses equally. Faye is entitled to a partnership salary of $6 000 per annum. The partnership has made a loss of $10 000 during its most recent financial year.

   What entry should be made in Kerron's current account for his share of the year's loss?

   A   Cr $5 000     B   Cr $8 000     C   Dr $5 000     D   Dr $8 000

16. Which of the following does **not** appear in the appropriation account of a limited company?

    A   debenture interest
    B   dividends paid
    C   retained earnings brought forward
    D   transfer to general reserve

17. Which of the following does **not** appear in the income statement of a cooperative society?

    A   auditors' fees
    B   interest received on investments
    C   membership fees
    D   secretary's honorarium

18. Which of the following should be included in the receipts and payments account of the local social club?

    I.   maintenance of club premises
    II.  repayment of loans
    III. subscriptions received in advance
        A   I and II only
        B   I and III only
        C   II and III only
        D   I, II and III

19. Which of the following is **not** shown in the overheads section of a manufacturing account?

    A   carriage outwards
    B   depreciation of machinery
    C   repairs to factory roof
    D   wages of production supervisors

20. Which of the following is a cash outflow to be included in a cash flow statement?

    A   credit purchases
    B   discounts received
    C   expenses due but not yet paid
    D   settlement of credit supplier's accounts

## Paper 2 questions

21. Joanna owns a retail business. She purchases all goods for resale on credit from one supplier, Lloyd's Wholesale Supplies. Sales are all on a cash basis. Joanna was preparing her books of account for October 2018. She has already completed the following books of original entry.

| Purchases book | | $ |
|---|---|---|
| Oct | 8   Lloyd's Wholesale Supplies | 2 600 |
|     | 23  Lloyd's Wholesale Supplies | 3 100 |
|     | Total purchases | 5 700 |

| Purchase returns book | | $ |
|---|---|---|
| Oct | 16  Lloyd's Wholesale Supplies | 140 |
|     | Total purchase returns | 140 |

The following balances appeared in the accounts on 1 October 2018.

|  | $ |
|---|---|
| Cash in hand | 180 |
| Cash at bank | 770 |
| Purchases ledger: Lloyd's Wholesale Supplies | 1200 |

Joanna has provided the following list of transactions to be recorded in her cash book.

Oct  2  Joanna withdrew cash $170 for private use
5  Paid Lloyd's Wholesale Supplies by cheque in settlement of the opening balance on their account less 5% cash discount
8  Cash sales totalled $3 520
9  Transferred cash $2 400 to the bank account
11  Purchased office equipment paying $800 by cheque
21  Paid Lloyd's Wholesale Supplies the amount due by cheque in settlement of the amount due at this date less 5% cash discount
24  Cash purchases $820
27  Paid rent $400 by cheque

a. Prepare the cash book for October 2018. Balance the cash book on 31 October 2018.
b. Prepare the account of Lloyd's Wholesale Supplies for October 2018. Balance the account on 31 October 2018.
c. Identify the source documents that will have been used for the transactions recorded in the cash book on (i) 9 October, (ii) 24 October.

22. Anthony owns a retail business. The following balances have been taken from his books of account at 31 July 2018, the last day of his financial year.

|  | $ |
|---|---|
| Administration expenses | 14830 |
| Carriage inwards | 3120 |
| Carriage outwards | 4450 |
| Delivery vehicles | |
| cost | 40000 |
| provision for depreciation, 1 August 2017 | 8000 |
| Discounts (credit balance) | 480 |
| Furniture and equipment at cost | |
| cost | 17000 |
| provision for depreciation, 1 August 2017 | 2550 |
| Interest received on investments | 1190 |
| Inventory, 1 August 2017 | 17200 |
| Purchases | 225300 |
| Rent | 22300 |
| Revenue | 381280 |
| Sales returns | 4720 |
| Wages and salaries | 44300 |

Additional information at 31 July 2018:

- Inventory was valued at $18 400.
- Interest on investments of $210 was due but not yet received.
- Wages due but not yet paid $730.
- Depreciation is provided at 20% per annum using the reducing-balance method on delivery vehicles, and at 15% per annum on furniture and equipment using the straight-line method.

    **a.** Explain why Anthony will have decided the reducing-balance method was appropriate for depreciating delivery vehicles.

    **b.** Prepare an income statement for the year ended 31 July 2018.

    Anthony is considered creating a provision for doubtful debts.

    **c.** Identify **two** accounting concepts which he will apply if he goes ahead with this idea.

    Last year Anthony's business had a net profit to revenue percentage of 12.22%.

    **d.** Calculate the net profit to revenue percentage for the year ended 31 July 2018.

    **e.** Describe **two** reasons which would explain why the net profit to revenue percentage has changed comparing the year ended 31 July 2018 with the year ended 31 July 2017.

**23.** Lisette has prepared a trial balance for her business. The trial balance totals did not agree and the difference of $290 was debited to a suspense account.

    **a.** Describe **one** type of error which would **not** be revealed by a trial balance. Give an example of this type of error.

    The following errors were discovered which accounted for the difference in the trial balance totals:

- An entry in the cash book for general expenses $60 had not been posted to the general ledger.
- The total of the sales returns book had been undercast by $190.
- $270 received from Grant Williams had been recorded correctly in the cash book but debited to the receivable's account in the sales ledger.

    **b.** Prepare journal entries to correct each of the errors. (Narratives are **not** required.)

    **c.** Prepare the suspense account recording the correction of the errors.

    Lisette has also been responsible for preparing a cash projection for each of the three months ending 31 March 2019. She has used the following details:

- Sales in cash are expected to be $4 000 in January 2019. This figure will increase by 10% each month compared to the previous month in February and March 2019.
- Payments for purchases of goods each month are expected to be 75% of the amount received for cash sales in that month.
- The business's expenses total $800 each month. This includes depreciation of non-current assets of $100 per month.
- In March 2019 it is planned to repay a bank loan of $2 400.
- The balance at bank on 1 January 2019 is forecast to be $900.

    **d.** Prepare a cash flow projection for each of the months January, February and March 2019.

**24.** Michelle and Nelson decided to go in to partnership and open a service business as bookkeepers on 1 January 2018.

  **a.** Describe **three** elements you would expect to find in the financial plan section of their business plan.

    At the end of their first year the business had made a net profit of $87 000. Their partnership agreement is as follows.

- Partners are to make fixed capital contributions of: Michelle $30 000, Nelson $50 000.
- Interest is to be charged at 8% on all drawings. Partners' drawings were: Michelle $21 000, Nelson $25 000.
- Partners are entitled to interest on their fixed capitals at 10% per annum.
- Michelle is to receive an annual salary of $12 000 for managing the business.
- Remaining profits and losses are to be shared in the ratio Michelle:Nelson, 3:2.

  **b.** Prepare the appropriation account for the year ended 31 December 2018.

  **c.** Prepare Nelson's current account for the year ended 31 December 2018. Balance the account at 31 December 2018.

    The partners employ Lincoln. Lincoln is paid $36 per hour for a 35-hour week. Overtime is paid at time and a half. Lincoln pays income tax at the rate of 20%; the personal allowance is $10 400 per annum. National insurance contributions are 5% of gross pay. He also pays $12 per week for membership of a health club.

  **d.** Calculate Lincoln's take-home pay for a week in which he worked for 38 hours.

**25.** BKG Ltd has an authorised capital of 1 600 000 ordinary shares of $1.50 each. Half of these shares had been issued at face value several years ago. The issue had been fully subscribed.

  **a.** Prepare a journal entry to record the issue of the ordinary shares. (Date and narrative are **not** required.)

    The company's appropriation account on 31 December 2018 was as follows.

Appropriation account for the year ended 31 December 2018

|  | $ | $ |
|---|---|---|
| Profit for the year |  | 255 000 |
| Less: |  |  |
| Dividends paid | 60 000 |  |
| Dividends proposed | 120 000 |  |
| Transfer to general reserve | 50 000 |  |
|  |  | 230 000 |
|  |  | 55 000 |
| Add: retained earnings at 1 January 2018 |  | 23 400 |
| Retained earnings at 31 December 2018 |  | 78 400 |

Other information available at 31 December 2018:

|  | $ |
|---|---|
| Accounts payable | 38 700 |
| Accounts receivable | 53 600 |
| Cash at bank | 41 700 |
| General reserve, 1 January 2018 | 72 000 |
| Insurance prepaid | 1 200 |
| Inventory, 31 December 2018 | 63 600 |
| Non-current assets net book value | 1 402 400 |
| Salaries due but unpaid | 3 400 |

b. Prepare a statement of financial position (balance sheet) at 31 December 2018.
c. Calculate the company's return on investment for the year ended 31 December 2018.
d. Identify **one** item you would expect to find in a co-operative society's appropriation account, which you would **not** expect to find in the appropriation account of a limited company.

## Chapter 1: Accounting as a profession

1. C    2. B    3. A    4. B    5. A

6. **Two from:** preparing accounts by entering and posting transactions; balancing accounts; preparing trial balances; verifying records and preparing reconciliation statements; storing documentation; payroll records; inventory records.

7. The purpose of accounting is to select, classify and summarise information (including preparing financial statements) for the benefit of owners and other users, so that they have the information they require to help manage a business and make effective decisions.

8. **Three from:** expertise in accounting skills and techniques; expertise in IT; analytical skills; leadership skills; communication skills.

9. A financial accountant summarises the organisation's financial position and provides information for key stakeholders, whereas a management accountant provides information for internal use to aid decision making and future planning.

10. Bookkeeping is the recording of financial information, particularly transactions, in a systematic way.

11. Confidentiality as an ethical principle in accounting means that you should not disclose information about the businesses/clients for whom you work to others without permission and should not use information for personal advantage. As an example, you would not discuss or gossip with friends about which local businesses are suffering a downturn and may have to close.

## Chapter 2: Accounting as a system

1. D    2. D    3. B    4. A    5. A
6. C    7. A    8. B    9. B    10. C

11. a. **One of:** QuickBooks; Sage; Xero; MYOB.
    b. **Benefits (two from):** increased accuracy; increased speed; improved accessibility; reduced staff costs; availability of more information (plus some development explaining each benefit).
    c. **Disadvantages (two from):** cost of equipment and software and updating; training costs; risks of data loss and breaches in security; maintenance costs (plus some development explaining each disadvantage).

12. a. The accounting cycle is the continuous sequence of activities which are required in order to record an organisation's financial transactions.
    b. i. $14 000    ii. $23 000    iii. $110 700

13. a. An asset is a resource owned by a business or money owed to the business by an external party.
    b. Total assets are $107 890, liabilities $29 400, so capital is $78 490.
    c. **Non-current assets:**
       shop premises $56 500, equipment $8 500, furniture and fittings $7 300 (subtotal $72 300)

**Current assets:**

inventory $14 990

accounts receivable $11 720

cash at bank $8 320

cash in hand $560 (subtotal $35 590)

Total assets $107 890

**Current liabilities:**

accounts payable $14 400

**Non-current liability:**

bank loan $15 000

**Capital:**

$78 490

**Total capital and liabilities:** $107 890

14. **a.** Liability is an amount owed by a business.

**b.** Assets $38 910, liabilities $22 710, so capital is $16 200.

**c.** **Current assets:** cash in hand $440, accounts receivable $2 820, inventory $18 350 (subtotal $21 610)
**Non-current assets:** equipment $5 400, shop furniture and fittings $11 900 (subtotal $17 300)
Total assets $38 910)

**Current liabilities:** bank overdraft $3,970, accounts payable $11 240, loan from JJL Finance $7 500 (subtotal $22 710)
Capital $16 200

**Total liabilities and capital:** $38 910

15. **a.** Assets $92 000, Capital $81 000, Liabilities $11 000

**b.** Assets $89 000, Capital $81 000, Liabilities $8 000

**c.** Assets $89 000, Capital $81 000, Liabilities $8 000

**d.** Assets $87 000, Capital $79 000, Liabilities $8 000

**e.** Assets $91 700, Capital $79 000, Liabilities $12 700

**f.** Assets $106 500, Capital $93 800, Liabilities $12 700

16. **a.** **Assets:** furniture and equipment $13 000, cash at bank $5 500, cash in hand $600 (total $19 100)
Capital $11 900; Liabilities: bank loan $7 200 (total $19 100)

**b.** **Feb 5: Assets:** furniture and equipment $17 000, cash at bank $5 500, cash in hand $600 (total $23 100)
Capital $11 900; Liabilities: bank loan $7 200, accounts payable $4 000 (total $23 100)

**Feb 9: Assets:** furniture and equipment $17 000, cash at bank $5 500, cash in hand $300 (total $22 800)
Capital $11,600; Liabilities: bank loan $7 200, accounts payable $4 000 (total $22 800)

Feb 11: **Assets:** furniture and equipment $17 000, cash at bank $5 700, cash in hand $100 (total $22 800)

Capital $11 600; Liabilities: bank loan $7 200, accounts payable $4 000 (total $22 800)

**Feb 15: Assets:** furniture and equipment $17 000, cash at bank $3 200, cash in hand $100 (total $20 300)

Capital $11 600; Liabilities: bank loan $7 200, accounts payable $1 500 (total $20 300)

**Feb 18: Assets:** furniture and equipment $17 000, cash at bank $5 200, cash in hand $100 (total $22 300)

Capital $11 600; Liabilities: bank loan $9 200, accounts payable $1 500 (total $22 300)

**Feb 23: Assets:** furniture and equipment $16 100, accounts receivable $900, cash at bank $5 200, cash in hand $100 (total $22 300)

Capital $11 600; Liabilities: bank loan $9 200, accounts payable $1 500 (total $22 300)

# Chapter 3: Books of original entry

| | | | | |
|---|---|---|---|---|
| 1. C | 2. B | 3. D | 4. C | 5. D |
| 6. B | 7. C | 8. C | 9. B | 10. B |

11. **a.** To encourage the customer to make a bulk purchase.

**b.** A debit note could be received from a customer to inform the business that some goods sold to the customer are being returned. The debit note is intended to prompt the business to send a credit note for the value of the returned goods.

**c.** **Purchases book:** TLZ Ltd $870, PXJ Ltd $3 600 (total $4 470)

**Sales book:** Leon's Retail Store $1 280, Hightown Stores $2 700 (total $3 980)

**Purchases returns book:** TLZ Ltd $60 (total $60)

**Sales returns book:** Leon's Retail Store $128 (total $128)

12. **a.** The possibility of a cash discount would be recorded on the invoice sent to the customer.

**b.** A discount received benefits a business as it is a reduction in the amount to be paid and is shown as income in the income statement. However, a discount received is only awarded where payment is made soon after the purchases has been made; this has a negative effect on a business's cash flow.

**c.** Dr side of cash book

**Discount allowed:** TBR Ltd $50

**Cash:** Opening balance b/d $175, Sales $3 460, Bank (contra) $420

**Bank:** TBR Ltd $1 350, Cash (contra) $3 300

Cr side of cash book

**Discount received:** GK Wholesale $40

**Cash:** general expenses $45, bank (contra) $3 300, Carnell Peters $80, balance c/d $630

**Bank:** opening balance b/d $1 560, drawings $320, GK Wholesale, $760, cash (contra) $420, balance c/d $1 590

(**Note:** the cash account has a debit closing balance b/d $630; the bank account has a debit closing balance b/d $1 590)

13. **a.** Imprest is the float – a fixed amount available for petty cash payments.

**b.** The analysis columns are used to total up the amount spent on various categories of expenditure. The totals are used to update the ledger accounts rather than transferring individual entries for each petty cash payment.

**c.** Petty cash account

Dr: opening balance $63, bank $137; closing balance b/d $52.90

Cr: travel $17.20, stationery $11.80, fuel $40.30, postage $8.40, taxi $18.10, printer paper $12.20, postage $5.60, fuel $33.50 (total $147.10)

Analysis column totals travel $35.30, stationery $24; fuel $73.80, postage $14.

(Note: the petty cash account has a closing debit balance b/d of $52.90)

**14. a.** The general journal is used to make a first record, in date order, of transactions which cannot be recorded in the other books of original entry.

**b.** Invoice for non-current asset.

**c.** **April 1:** Dr Bank $4 470, furniture and equipment $11 840; Cr bank loan $5 000, capital $11 310 (entries to record the opening of books of account)

**April 12:** Dr Furniture $5 600; Cr RK Supplies Ltd $5 600 (entries to record purchase of non-current asset on credit)

**April 21:** Dr Cash $10, Cr wages $10 (correction of entries made to record payment of wages)

**April 25:** Dr RK Supplies Ltd $630, Cr Furniture $630 (entries to record the return of non-current asset purchased on credit).

**15. a.** The books of original entry are used to make a first record, in date order, of information recorded on source documents.

**b.** **Purchases book:** PT Supplies Ltd $3 520 (total $3 520)

**Sales book:** Sharon Williams $820 (total $820)

**Purchases returns book:** PT Supplies Ltd $120 (total $120)

**Sales returns book:** Sharon Williams $40 (total $40)

**General journal:** Dr discounts received $40; Cr FQ Wholesale $40 (entries to cancel discounts received)

Cash book debit side:

**Discounts allowed:** Sharon Williams $39 (total $39)

**Cash:** opening balance b/d $380, sales $3 490 (total $3 870)

**Bank:** opening balance b/d $1 990, Cash (contra) $3,000, Sharon Williams $741 (total $5 731)

Cash book credit side:

**Discounts received:** FQ Wholesale $40 (total $40)

**Cash:** bank (contra) $3,000, office expenses $80, closing balance c/d $790 (total $3 870)

**Bank:** FQ Wholesale $1 560, closing balance c/d $4 171 (total $5 731)

(Note the cash account has a closing debit balance b/d of $790; the bank account has a closing debit balance b/d of $4 171)

## Chapter 4: Ledgers and the trial balance

**1.** A    **2.** C    **3.** C    **4.** A    **5.** C

**6.** A    **7.** D    **8.** A    **9.** B    **10.** D

**11. a.** A real account is an asset whereas a nominal account records expenses and income (i.e. losses and gains).

**b.** Purchases ledger

**XQ Manufacturers:** Dr Purchases returns $490; Cr Purchases $3 650, Purchases $1 830

**Island Autos:** Dr Purchases returns $380; Cr Purchases $4 490

Sales ledger

**Ford Retail Unit:** Dr Sales $880, Sales $2 390; Cr Sales returns $220

**Woodland Stores:** Dr Sales $3 170, Cr Sales returns $170

General ledger

**Purchases:** Dr purchases book $9 970

**Sales returns:** Dr sales returns book $390

**Purchases returns:** Cr purchases returns book $810

**Sales:** Cr sales book $6 440

**12. a.** Folio references are used to provide a link between entries in the books of original entry and the ledger accounts. They are useful when it is necessary to trace back information about an entry.

   **b.** **i.** 5% (i.e. 4 × 100/80)     **ii.** 2% (i.e. 70 × 100/1400)

   **c.** Sales ledger

   Beacon Stores

   Dr Balance b/d $1 400, sales book $1 310, sales book $1 960, discount allowed $28

   Cr sales returns book $110, bank $1 372, discounts allowed $28, balance c/d $3,188

   (Note: the account has a balance b/d on Oct 1 of $3 188)

   RJ Ltd

   Dr Balance b/d $80, sales book $590, sales book $840

   Cr Cash $76, discounts allowed $4, sales returns book $30, bank $1 330, discounts allowed $70

   (Note: the account has no closing balance)

**13. a.** Trial balances do not reveal every error that can occur. For example, trial balances do not reveal errors such as commission/complete reversal/omission/original entry principle/compensating.

   **b.** To provide information for the preparation of financial statements which can be easily accessed.

   **c.** Trial balance

   **Dr entries:** carriage inwards $710, carriage outwards $450, discounts allowed $550, drawings $18 320, general expenses $7 280, non-current assets $48 500, petty cash in hand $30, purchases $127 900, sales returns $840, wages $22 400

   **Cr entries:** bank overdraft $380, capital $47 650, discounts received $420, loan from TZ Finance $8 000, purchases returns $630, revenue $169 900

   Totals $226 980

**14. a.** **Andrew Grant:**

   July 1 Shenika owed $4 920, 14th purchased goods on credit $3 860, 21st returned goods outwards $80, 28th settled $4 000 of amount due by cheque less a 5% discount received; 31st balance amount owed $4 700

   **b.** **Lisa Marks**

   July 15 Shenika sold goods $60, 25th the amount due was settled in cash $57 having deducted a cash discount allowed of $3.

c. **Non-current assets**

   July 1 Shenika owned non-current assets $27 500; 27th purchased additional non-current assets on credit from HW Stores $3 600, closing balance non-current assets owned $31 100.

15. a. Journal

   1st Dr bank $8 000, non-current assets $38 000; Cr loan $12 000, capital $34 000

   b. Journal (continued)

   16th Dr non-current assets $1 800; Cr RTV Supplies $1 800

   23rd Dr RTV Supplies $220; Cr non-current assets $220

   Purchases book

   4th WV Manufacturers $7 200; total $7 200

   Sales returns book

   17th Kathy's General Store $110; total $110

   Purchases returns book

   8th WV Manufacturers $192; total $192

   Sales book

   11th Kathy's General Stores $1 890; total $1 890

   Cash book (debit side)

   **Discounts allowed:** 28th Kathy's General Stores $30 (total $30)

   **Cash:** 3rd bank $800, 24th sales $4 360

   **Bank:** 1st journal $8 000, 27th cash $4 000, 28th Kathy's General Stores $1 750

   Cash book (credit side)

   **Discounts received:** 21st WV Manufacturers $200 (total $200)

   **Cash:** 7th purchases $220, 19th general expenses $140, 27th bank $4 000

   **Bank:** 3rd cash $800, 14th drawings $320, 21st WV Manufacturers $3 800

   (Note: there are closing debit balances: cash 800 and bank $8 830)

   c. **Purchases ledger:**

   **WV Manufacturers:** Dr 8th purchases returns $192, 21st bank $3 800, 21st discount received $200; Cr 4th purchases $7 200

   **RTV Supplies:** Dr 23rd non-current assets $220; Cr 16th non-current assets $1 800

   Sales ledger

   **Kathy's General Store:** Dr 11th sales $1 890; Cr 17th sales returns $110, 28th bank $1 750, 28th discounts allowed $30

   General ledger

   **Capital:** Cr 1st journal $34 000

   **Discounts allowed:** Dr 30th cash book $30

   **Discounts received:** Cr 30th cash book $200

   **Drawings:** Dr 14th bank $320

   **General expenses:** Dr 19th cash $140

**Loan:** Cr 1st $12 000

**Non-current assets:** Dr 1st journal $38 000, 16th RTV Supplies $1 800; Cr 23rd RTV Supplies $220

**Purchases:** Dr 7th cash $220; 30th purchases book $7 200

**Sales returns:** Dr 30th sales returns book $110

**Purchases returns:** Cr 30th purchases returns book $192

**Sales:** Cr 24th cash $4 360; 30th sales book $1 890

d.  Trial balance

**Dr entries:** cash $800, bank $8,830, drawings $320, discounts allowed $30, general expenses $140, non-current assets $39 580, purchases $7 420, sales returns $110

**Cr entries:** capital $34 000, discounts received $200, loan $12 000, purchases returns $192, sales $6 250, WV Manufacturers $3 008, RTV Supplies $1 580

**Totals:** $57 230

# Chapter 5: The preparation and analysis of financial statements of the sole trader

| 1. C | 2. A | 3. C | 4. C | 5. D |
|------|------|------|------|------|
| 6. D | 7. D | 8. D | 9. D | 10. C |

11. a.  Both are expenses, but carriage inwards is the delivery cost added to a business's purchases and is charged to the trading section of the income statement, whereas carriage outwards is the cost of delivery goods to customers and is charged as a selling expenses to the profit and loss section of the income statement.

b.  Revenue $281 920 less sales returns $3 210 (subtotal $278 710) less cost of sales made up of opening inventory $14 400 plus purchases $182 650 less purchases returns $2 770 plus carriage inwards $3 360 (subtotal $197 640) less closing inventory $18 310 (subtotal, cost of sales $179 330); gross profit $99 380

12. a.  **Inventory account:** Dr Sept 1 2017 opening balance b/d $20 320, 31 Aug 2018 income statement $19 330; Cr 31 Aug 2018 income statement $20 320

b.  **Trading section:** Revenue $189 940 less sales returns $2 290 (subtotal $187 650) less cost of sales made up of opening inventory $20 320 plus purchases $112 200 less purchases returns $3 020 (subtotal $129 500) less closing inventory $19 330 (subtotal, cost of sales $110 170) gross profit $77 480 plus discounts received $210 (subtotal $77 690) less expenses made up of carriage outwards $890, discounts allowed $320, electricity charges $1 770, insurance $640, repairs and maintenance charges $1 830, salaries $40 400, water charges $1 450 (subtotal, total expenses $47 300); net profit $30 390

13. a.  i.  A non-current asset is a resource owned by a business which will benefit the business for more than one year;

ii. a current asset is a resource owned by a business which will benefit the business for less than one year.

b.  **Non-current assets:** buildings $122 000, delivery vehicles $28 400, furniture and equipment $9 640 (subtotal $160 040)

**Current assets:** inventory $31 370, accounts receivable $8 080, cash at bank $1 260, cash in hand $190 (subtotal $40 900)

**Current liabilities:** loan from Antonio $600, accounts payable $14 650 (subtotal $15 250)

**Non-current liabilities:** bank loan $8 300

**Totals:** $177 390

**Capital:** opening balance $198 540 less drawings $17 330, less net loss $3 820 (subtotal $177 390)

**14. a.** Working capital is net current assets. It is the resources which are available to run the business efficiently on a day-to-day basis. If the amount is too low the business could fail; if the amount is too large then resources are being wasted.

**b.** Revenue $246 300 less sales returns $2 220 (subtotal $244 080) less cost of sales made up of opening inventory $14 490 plus purchases $152 570 less purchases returns $1 040 plus carriage inwards $1 160 (subtotal $167 180) less closing inventory $12 320 (subtotal, cost of sales $154 860); gross profit $89 220 add discounts received $220 (subtotal $89 440) less expenses made up of discounts allowed $350, general expenses $3 320, insurance $510, loan interest $840, vehicle running costs $4 870, wages $38 200 (subtotal, total expenses $48,090) net profit $41 350

**c. Non-current assets:** $85 000

**Current assets:** inventory $12 320, accounts receivable $9 980 (subtotal $22 300)

**Current liabilities:** accounts payable $11 480, bank overdraft $440 (subtotal $11 920)

**Non-current liability:** loan from KLQ Finance $12 500

**Total:** $82 880

**Capital:** opening balance $70 000 add net profit $41 350 less drawings $28 470 (subtotal $82 880)

**15. a.**
- **Gross profit percentage:** gross profit × 100/revenue; $160 000 × 100/$400 000 = 40%
- **Mark-up percentage:** gross profit × 100/cost of sales; $160 000 × 100/$240 000 = 66.67%
- **Rate of inventory turnover:** cost of sales/average inventory; $240 000/$24 000 = 10 times
- **Net profit percentage:** net profit × 100/revenue: $60 000 × 100/$400 000 = 15%
- **General expenses to revenue percentage:** general expenses × 100/revenue = $40 000 × 100/$400 000 = 10%
- **Wages of assistants to revenue percentage:** wages × 100/revenue = $60 000/$400 000 = 15%

**16. a.** Working capital $14 000

**b.**
- **Current ratio:** current assets/current liabilities; $35 000/$21,000 = 1.67:1
- **Acid test ratio:** current assets less inventory/current liabilities; $18 000/$21 000 = 0.86:1
- **Return on investment percentage:** net profit × 100/opening capital; $52 000 × 100/$200 000 = 26%
- **Accounts receivable collection period:** accounts receivable × 365/credit sales; $14 000 × 365/$159 700 = 32 days
- **Accounts payable payment period:** accounts payable × 365/credit purchases; $21 000 × 365/$219 000 = 35 days

**17. a.** Gross profit percentage.

**b.** Rate of inventory turnover; net profit percentage.

**c.** Although the business has been making more gross profit in relation to sales, the business's expenses must have been increasing at an even faster rate. This is a sign of not running the business efficiently.

**d.** Rate of inventory turnover could be improved by (two from): reducing average inventory (this could also lead to reduced storage costs and reduced chance of inventory wastage); reducing selling prices and making the business more competitive; increasing spending on marketing/advertising to boost sales.

**18. a.** Improvement in return on investment could have arisen because the capital invested in the business has been reduced.

**b.** The current ratio has decreased over the three years. The business's ability to meet its liabilities will have reduced. It will have less resources to meet medium-term commitments such as paying credit suppliers, providing for drawings, making loan repayments, etc.

**c.** The acid test ratio has increased. The business has more resources to meet its immediate commitments such as everyday expenses, payments to credit suppliers, etc.

**d.** The current ratio could be improved by (two from): reducing drawings; introducing extra capital; taking out a long-term loan; increasing profits.

**19. a.** Business A has a higher gross profit percentage than the other businesses; it controls its running costs more effectively than the other businesses.

**b.** The current ratio is higher than the average for this type of business. This means it is wasting some resources which are unnecessarily tied up in working capital.

**c.** The current ratio is lower than the average for this type of business. This means Business C is more likely to have difficulty meeting its medium-term commitments.

**d.** Credit customers are settling their accounts more slowly than Business B is paying its credit suppliers. This will put a strain on the business's cash flow.

**20. a.**
- Gross profit percentage: 2017, 22.5%; 2018, 25%
- Net profit percentage: 2017, 12.5%; 2018, 10.67%
- Return on investment percentage: 2017, 20%; 2018 18.46%

**b.** There is a mixed picture, but on the whole the business's performance has declined. The business has increased its sales by 12.5% comparing 2018 with 2017 perhaps this has resulted from reducing selling prices or maybe there is less competition from rival businesses. The gross profit percentage has improved (a strength) – perhaps cheaper suppliers of goods for resale have been found. Despite the improvement in revenue and gross profit, the business's net profit percentage has decreased (a weakness) indicating that costs are not being controlled so efficiently. The return on investment percentage has also decreased (a weakness) perhaps because net profits had been reduced.

**c.** Costs need to be controlled more effectively by reducing unnecessary expenditure and wastage; increase the gross profit percentage even more by increasing selling prices or improved advertising.

# Chapter 6: Accounting adjustments

1. D     2. B     3. C     4. A     5. B
6. C     7. D     8. C     9. A     10. A

11. **a.** Accruals concept ensures profits for a year are based on matching income for that year with expenses for that year whether or not amounts involved have been actually received or paid.

    **b.** **Journal:** Dr Income statement; Cr insurance $4 460; Dr Income statement, Cr wages of assistants $38 110; Dr loan interest received, Cr income statement $1 610; Dr rent received, Cr income statement $3 230.

    **c.** **Insurance account:** Dr Bank $4 820; Cr Income statement $4 460, Balance c/d $360 (the account will have a debit balance b/d $360)
    **Wages of assistants:** Dr Bank $36 880, balance c/d $1 230; Cr Income statement $38 110 (the account will have a credit balance b/d $1 230)
    **Loan interest account:** Dr Income statement $1 610; Credit Bank $1 450, Balance c/d $160 (the account will have a debit balance b/d $160)
    **Rent received:** Dr Income statement $3 230; balance c/d $490; Cr Bank $3 720 (the account will a credit balance b/d $490)

    **d.** Insurance prepaid, current asset; wages due but unpaid, current liability; loan interest due but not received, current asset; rent received in advance, current liability.

12. **a.** A bad debt is an amount owed by a credit customer which will not be paid.

    **b.** **Two from:** credit customer disputes amount due; the customer cannot be traced; the customer is unable to pay because of lack of funds/bankruptcy.

    **c.** **Journal:** Dr bad debts, Cr Hightown Fashions $1 480 (narrative: entries to write off bad debt).

    **d.** **Hightown Fashions account:** Dr Sales $1 480, Cr bad debts $1 480

    **e.** Accruals (or matching) concept and prudence concept.

    **f.** Dr income statement, Cr provision for doubtful debts.

13. **a.** **Two from:** past experience; advice from accountant; analysis of the age of outstanding debts

    **b.** Journal Dr provision for doubtful debts; Cr income statement $70 (narrative: entries to decrease provision for doubtful debts).

    **c.** Provision for doubtful debts account
    **2017:** Dr income statement $70, balance c/d $530; Cr Balance b/d $600
    **2018;** Dr balance c/d $780; Cr Balance b/d $530, income statement $250
    (the account is completed with a credit balance b/d $780 on 1 Jan 2019)

14. **a.** "nbv" means net book value – that is the cost of a non-current asset less the accumulated depreciation charges on a particular date.

    **b.** **Journal:** Dr income statement; Cr provision for depreciation, computer equipment $3 600

    **c.** Computer equipment account
    Dr Bank $18 000, Technoplus Ltd $14 000; Cr balance c/d $32 000 (the account is completed with a debit balance b/d $32 000 on 1 Jan 2019)
    Provision for depreciation (computer equipment) account
    Dr Balance c/d $9 300; Cr Income statement (2017) $3 600, Income statement (2018) $5 700

(the account is completed with a credit balance b/d $9300) [Workings: depreciation 31 Dec 2018 is $3600 (original equipment) plus ¾ × 20% × $14000 (additional equipment) = $5700]

d. **Extract:** non-current assets cost $32000, total depreciation $9300, net $22700

15. a. i. Capital expenditure means payments made to acquire or improve non-current assets/expenditure from which benefits last for more than one year;

ii. example – any non-current asset.

b. i. Revenue expenditure means payments made for the day-to-day running of a business/expenditure from which the benefit lasts for less than one year;

ii. example – any expense.

c. The wages are debited to the machinery account because they should be regarded as capital expenditure. The benefit to the business from the payment of the wages will last as long as the machinery is in use.

d. i. Capital expenditure; delivery vehicle, alterations, logo painted on vehicle;

ii. Revenue expenditure; insurance.

e. Correct identification is important to ensure profits, asset values and capital are accurately stated.

16. Revenue $212000; less cost of sales – opening inventory $18490 plus (purchases $117400 less purchases returns $820) $116580, less closing inventory $19670; gross profit $96600, add discounts received $580 plus loan interest received ($380 + $80) $460 (subtotal $97640) less expenses – bad debts written off $410, carriage outwards $770, depreciation of non-current assets (20% × $84000) $16800, increase in provision for doubtful debts $90, rent ($11940 – $1840) $10100, wages and salaries $46470 (subtotal of expenses $74640); net profit $23000

17. a. A provision for doubtful debts ensures that a true and fair value is shown for accounts receivable on a statement of financial position (balance sheet) in accordance with the prudence concept.

b. **Non-current assets:** cost $125000 less total depreciation $37500, net $87500
**Current assets:** inventory $11730, accounts receivable ($7400 less provision for doubtful debts $370) $7030, insurance prepaid $380 (subtotal $19140)
**Less Current liabilities:** accounts payable $10260, general expenses accrual $450, rent received in advance $770, bank overdraft $1090 (subtotal $12570)
**Capital:** opening balance $84000, net profit $46910 less drawings $26840 (subtotal $94070)

18. a. **One of:** the estimated economic life of the non-current asset; the residual value of the non-current asset; whether the depreciation charge should be constant or gradually diminishing.

b. **Income statement:** gross profit $137300 add rent received $5820 [$6620 – (1/3 × $2400)] decrease in provision for doubtful debts $60 [$930 – (5% × $17400)], discounts received $780; subtotal $143960 less administration expenses ($13920 – $560) $13360, bad debts $860, bank loan interest $480 [$400 + (1/6 × 8% × $6000)], depreciation buildings (2% × $185000) $3700, depreciation delivery vehicles $9000 [25% × ($48000 – $12000)], discounts allowed $590, electricity charges $5520, repairs and maintenance $4480, wages $52550 (subtotal expenses $90540), net profit $53420

c. Statement of financial position (balance sheet)

**Non-current assets:** buildings cost $185 000, total depreciation $18 500, net $166 500; delivery vehicles cost $48 000, total depreciation $21 000, net $27 000 (subtotal $193 500)

**Current assets:** inventory $33 850, accounts receivable $16 530 ($17 400 less provision for doubtful debts $870), administration expenses prepaid $560, cash at bank $8 240 (subtotal $59 180)

**Current liabilities:** bank loan $6 000, accounts payable $23 380, rent received in advance $800, interest due $80 (subtotal $30 260)

**Capital:** opening balance $192 100 add net profit $53 420 less drawings $23 100 (subtotal $222 420)

19. a. **Total cost of equipment:** original $49 500 + additional $18 000 + carriage $500 = $68 000

b. **Depreciation charge:** 15% × $68 000 = $10 200

c. **Income statement:** revenue $399 320 ($403 200 − returns $3 880) less cost of sales $270 500 [opening inventory $17 420 + purchases $269 220 ($272 300 − returns $4 250 + carriage inwards $1 170) − closing inventory $16 140]; gross profit $128 820 less electricity charges $5 690, insurance ($3 440 − $670 prepaid) $2 770, office expenses $5 510, rent $13 700 [$14 900 + (1/3 × $3 600)], wages and salaries $51 300, provision for doubtful debts (4% × $12 000) $480, provision for depreciation of equipment $10 200 (subtotal expenses $89 650); net profit $39 170

20. a. **Income statement:** revenue $125 610 + rent receivable ($1 850 − $290 received in advance) $1 560 + decrease in provision for doubtful debts $70 (subtotal $127 240) less expenses, bad debts $120, insurance ($8 320 − $190 prepaid) $8 130, motor vehicle running expenses $11 490, motor vehicle repairs $3 940, office expenses ($840 + $140 due) $980, wages and salaries $25 360, depreciation premises $6 900, furniture and equipment (20% × $6 300) $1 260, motor vehicles (nbv $76 000 × 20%) $15 200 (subtotal expenses $73 380), net profit $53 860

b. Statement of financial position (balance sheet)

**Non-current assets:** premises cost $230 000, total depreciation $13 800, net $216 200; motor vehicles cost $95 000, total depreciation $34 200, net $60 800; furniture and equipment cost $6 300, total depreciation $2 520, net $3 780 (subtotal $280 780)

**Current assets:** accounts receivable ($4 800 less provision for doubtful debts $140) $4 660, insurance prepaid $190, cash at bank $7 890, cash in hand $320 (subtotal $13 060)

**Current liabilities:** accounts payable $880, office expenses due $140, rent received in advance $290 (subtotal $1 310)

**Capital:** opening balance $270 000 add net profit $53 860, less drawings $31 330 (subtotal $292 530)

# Chapter 7: Control systems

| 1. A | 2. D | 3. D | 4. B | 5. A |
|------|------|------|------|------|
| 6. A | 7. B | 8. D | 9. B | 10. C |

11. a. Checks arithmetical accuracy of the double entry; provides a summary of account balances which can be easily accessed when preparing financial statements.

b. i. Error of commission

ii. Error of omission

    **iii.** Error of commission

    **iv.** Error of principle

    **v.** Error of original entry

  **c.** Dr motor repair $480, Cr rent and rates $480.

    Dr insurance $1 260, Cr bank account $1 260.

    Dr Suzanne Ellis account $415, Cr Susan Ellis account $415.

    Dr plant and machinery $1 450, Cr repairs and maintenance $1 450.

    Dr Paper Supplies Ltd account $90, Cr stationery $90.

**12. a. i.** Error of commission occurs when an entry is made for the right amount on the correct side but of the wrong account within the same class; error of principle is also made for the right amount on the correct side but within the wrong class of account. (Plus an example of each to develop the answer.)

    **ii.** Error of omission occurs when a transaction is completed omitted from the books of account; error of original entry occurs when the amount shown on a source document is misread and the entries made are for the wrong amount in books of account. (Plus an example of each to develop the answer.)

  **b.** Dr sales $200, Cr suspense account $200.

    Dr suspense account $130, Cr interest received $130.

    Dr postage $25, Cr suspense account $25.

    Dr Dorsey Ltd $105, Cr suspense account $105.

  **c.** Debit

    Balance b/d $200; interest received $130; total $330.

    Credit

    Sales $200; Postage $25, Dorsey Ltd $105; total $330

**13. a.** A suspense account is a temporary account used to record the difference in the totals of a trial balance and entries arising from corrections made to correct errors which caused the difference.

  **b.** Dr repairs $440, Cr suspense account $440.

    Dr suspense account $100, Cr sales $100.

    Dr suspense account $290, Cr Ingrid account $290.

  **c.** Debit

    Balance b/d $50; sales $100; Ingrid $290; total $440.

    Cr repairs $440; total $440.

**14. a.** When an error of complete reversal occurs, it is necessary to make an entry to cancel the wrong entries and also to make the same entries to record the correct entries, hence twice the amount is involved.

  **b.** Dr Clifton sales ledger account $360, Cr Cleavon sales ledger account $360.

    Dr discounts received $200, Cr suspense account $200.

    Dr bank account $240, Cr interest received $240.

    Dr motor repairs $20, Cr suspense account $20.

  **c.** Debit

Balance b/d $220; total $220

Cr discounts received $200; motor repairs $20; total $220

**15. a.** Example will be of an error which affects an account which is not transferred to the income statement.

  **b.** Profit per income statement $38 300 + rent $2 500 − revenue $1 900 − depreciation $4 800 − advertising $300 = revised net profit for the year $33 800.

**16. a.** Error type, one of: commission, omission, original entry, compensating, principle, complete reversal (plus an example for one type)

  **b.** Loss per income statement ($2 700) + discount received $1 400 + heat and light $500 + sales $13 600 − bank interest $800 + rent $4 500 = revised net profit for the year $16 500.

**17. a.** A direct debit is an instruction to a bank to make payments on behalf of one of the bank's customers of amounts requested up to a specified limit. A standing order is similar except that the amount concerned is fixed and the timing of the payment is at regular intervals.

  **b.** When making the comparison it is a good idea to tick the items which appear in both documents.

  **c.** Cash book update:

Dr opening balance $5 161, credit transfer C Thomas $390

Cr Regional Telecoms $220, charges $54, closing balance c/d $5 277

(Note the closing balance b/d will appear as a debit entry)

  **d.** Bank reconciliation statement (version 1)

Balance as per cash book $5 277, add unpresented cheques ($833, $1 380) $2 213, less late lodgements $1 230, balance as per bank statement $6 260

Bank reconciliation statement (version 2)

Balance as per bank statement $6 260, less unpresented cheques $2 313, add late lodgements $1 230, balance as per cash book $5 277

**18. a.** **Two from:**

- It helps check the accuracy of the cash book by ensuring that, once timing differences are taken into account, the cash book balance and the bank statement balance agree.
- Results in the cash book being fully updated with information shown on a bank statement which had been overlooked.
- It helps reduce the chance of fraud because the cash book is compared with the independently prepared bank statement.

  **b.** Cash book update

Dr opening balance $2 382, credit transfer $441

Cr bank charges $84, SO rent $485, drawings $18, balance c/d $2 236

(Note: the closing balance b/d will appear as a debit entry)

  **c.** Bank reconciliation statement (version 1)

Balance as per cash book $2 236, add unpresented cheque $332, less late lodgement $1 432, add error in bank statement $132, balance as per bank statement $1 268

Bank reconciliation statement (version 2)

Balance as per bank statement $1 268, less error in bank statement $132, less unpresented cheques $332, add late lodgement $1 432, balance as per cash book $2 236

**19. a.** In the cash book the bank account is an asset account and so any decrease in the asset is shown as a credit entry; the bank's record is a liability account (as the bank owed any positive balance to the customer) and so any decrease in the liability is shown as a debit balance.

**b.** Cash book update

Dr credit transfer $480, balance c/d $2 217

Cr opening balance $2 360, charges $139, error sales $198

(Note: the closing balance b/d will appear as a credit entry)

**c.** Current liability – bank overdraft $2 217

**d.** Bank reconciliation statement (version 1)

Balance as per cash book overdrawn $2 217, unpresented cheques ($1 397, $300) $1 697, subtotal overdrawn $520; late lodgement $375, balance as per bank statement $895 (overdrawn).

Bank reconciliation statement (version 2)

Balance as per bank statement $895 (overdrawn); unpresented cheques $1 697, subtotal $2 592 (overdrawn), late lodgement $375, balance as per cash book $2 217 (overdrawn)

**20. a.** **Two from:** Provides a check on the arithmetical accuracy of the purchases and sales ledger; provides totals of accounts payable and accounts receivable for inclusion in a trial balance which are obtained quickly; helps reduce the chance of fraud as the purchases and sales ledgers are subject to an independent check.

**b.** Accounts payable control account

Dr discounts received $472, payments $14 950, purchases returns $589, closing balance c/d $9 236

Cr opening balance $8 920, Cr purchases $16 327

(Note: the closing balance b/d will appear as a credit entry)

**c.** Accounts receivable control account

Dr opening balance $11 420, credit sales $20 445

Cr discounts allowed $11 430, receipts $22 748, sales returns $491, closing balance c/d $7 756

(Note: the closing balance b/d will appear as a debit entry)

**21. a.** The details in the list will have been obtained from the books of original entry.

**b.** Accounts receivable control account

Dr opening balance $23 786, Cr sales 85 492, interest charged on overdue accounts $256, refunds on accounts overpaid $163, dishonoured cheques $827, closing balance c/d $620

Cr opening balance $1 034, bad debts written off $2 824, contra $440, discounts allowed $3 721, receipts $82 142, sales returns $3 462, closing balance c/d $17 521

(Note: there will be a debit balance b/d of $17 521 and a credit balance b/d of $620)

**22. a.** A contra entry is made when a customer is also a supplier of a business. If the contra entry is between the purchases and sales ledger accounts, it means the balance in the sales ledger is greater than the balance in the purchases ledger before the transfer is made.

**b.** Accounts payable control account

Dr opening balance $414, contra $620, discounts received $561, payments $24 372, purchases returns $1 927, closing balance c/d $4 507

Cr opening balance $8 450, Cr purchases $23 726, closing balance c/d $225

(Note: the closing balance b/d of $225 will appear as a debit entry; the closing balance b/d of $4 507 will appear as a credit entry)

**c.** The conclusions are that there are errors in the accounts, and those errors could be in the sales ledger, the accounts receivable control account, or both.

**d.** Credit sales debit entry, discounts allowed credit entry, contra credit entry.

## Chapter 8: Accounting for partnerships

**1.** B    **2.** C    **3.** A    **4.** B    **5.** B    **6.** B

**7. a. Two advantages:** opportunity to share ideas and skills; opportunity to share responsibility and workload

**b. One disadvantage:** possibility of slow decision making; possibility of serious disagreement leading to poor business performance; partnership may be short-lived if a partner retires or dies

**c.** Appropriation account for year ended 30 November 2018
Profit $74 000

**Deductions:** salary (Elizabeth) $8 000; interest on capitals (Elizabeth $6 400, Marcus $4 000) $10 400; share of residual profit (Elizabeth 3/5 $33 360, Marcus 2/5 $22 240) $55 600

**8. a.** A deed of partnership will ensure that partners have considered and agreed how profits and losses should be shared and so partners will avoid disputes over this vital matter.

**b.** Residual profit = $38 600 + interest on drawings $1 460 = $40 060 − salary $18 000 − interest on capital $15 600 = $6 460

**Shares:** Rashan $3 230; Vishon $3 230

**c.** Current accounts:
**Rashan:**
Dr opening balance b/d $4 500, interest on drawings $640, drawings $16 000

Cr salary $18 000, interest on capital $8 200, share of residual profit $3 230, closing balance c/d $8 290

(Note: closing balance b/d $8 290 will be a debit entry)
**Vishon:**
Dr interest on drawings $820, drawings $20 500, closing balance c/d $4 490

Cr opening balance b/d $6 200, interest on capital $7 400, share of residual profit $3 230, closing balance c/d $4 490

(Note: closing balance b/d $4 490 will be a credit entry)

**d.** Rashan owes the partnership $8 290; Vishon is owed $4 490 by the partnership

9.  **a.** A partner's loan interest should be debited to the income statement and credited to the partner's current account (or capital account if current accounts are not used).

    **b.** **Calculation of profit shares:** net profit $11,000 – partnership salaries $18 000 = residual loss of $7 000 – shared André 4/10 $2 800, Beverley 3/10 $2 100, Calvin 3/10 $2 100
    Capital accounts

    **André:**
    Dr drawings $21 200, residual loss $2 800, closing balance c/d $58 500
    Cr opening balance b/d $82 500

    **Beverley:**
    Dr drawings $19 900, residual loss $2 100, closing balance c/d $61 100
    Cr opening balance b/d $73 100, salary $10 000

    **Calvin**
    Dr drawings $18 400, residual loss $2 100, closing balance c/d $42 800
    Cr opening balance b/d $55 300, salary $8 000

    (Note: the closing balance b/d on each capital account will be credit entries)

10. **a.** **Two from:** the limited partner cannot take part in the day-to-day running or management of the business; the limited partner's capital contribution cannot be reduced; there must be at least one "general partner"; the business must be formally registered as a limited partnership.

    **b.** **Profit shares:** interest on capital (Anika $6 000, Shauna $5 000), residual profit $31 400 (shares Anika $15 700, Shauna $15 700)

    **c.** Statement of financial position (balance sheet) at 31 December 2018
    Non-current assets $87 300; current assets (inventory $14 200, accounts receivable $8 300, prepayments $700, cash at bank $3 200) subtotal $26 400

    less current liabilities (accounts payable $6 500, accruals $600) subtotal $7 100; net current assets/working capital $19 300; total $106 600

    **Capital accounts:** Anika $60 000, Shaua $50 000 – total $110 000
    Current accounts:

    **Anika:** add interest on capital $6 000 + residual profit $15 700, subtotal $21 700 less opening balance $600 and drawings $21 200, closing balance debit $100
    **Shauna:** opening balance $2 500 + interest on capital $5 000 + residual profit $15 700, subtotal $23 200 less drawings $26 500, net $3 300 (debit balance)
    Total $106 600

11. **a.** Profits and losses should be shared equally where there is no agreement.

    **b.** **Journal entry:**
    Dr motor vehicles $29 400, inventory $11 900, accounts receivables $4 800, bank $3 900
    Cr capital $35 400, bank loan $8 000, accounts payable $6 600

    **Narrative:** entries to record Grace's contributions to the partnership

    **c.** Statement of financial position (balance sheet) at 1 January 2019
    **Non-current assets:** motor vehicles $29 400, furniture and equipment $18 300 (subtotal $47 700)

**Current assets:** inventory $19 300, accounts receivable $10 700 (subtotal $30 000)
**Capitals:** Grace $35 400, Kenton $19 800 (subtotal $55 200)
**Non-current liability:** bank loan $8 000
**Current liabilities:** accounts payable $12 900, bank overdraft $1 600 (subtotal $14 500)
**Total:** $77 700

**12. a.** In a partnership, the lack of limited liability means that each partner is responsible for the debts of the business, and each partner is at risk of losing not only their investment in the business, but their private possessions as well should the partnership business fail.

**b.** Income statement for the year ended 30 September 2018.
Revenue $139 910 less sales returns $830 (subtotal $139 080)

**Less cost of sales:** opening inventory $14 440 + purchases $83 450 – closing inventory $11 250 (subtotal $86 640)
Gross profit $52 440
**Less expenses:** administration $3 640 + carriage outwards $1 430 + insurance ($3 410 – $290) $3 120 + loan interest Steve $900 + wages ($29 620 + $430) $30 050 + depreciation (20% × $32 000) $6 400 (subtotal $45 540)
Net profit $6 900

**c.** Appropriation account for year ended 30 September 2018
Net profit $6 900
Add interest on drawings (Kathy $2 320, Steve $1 780) $4 100
Less interest on capitals (Kathy $7 200, Steve $5 600) $12 800, salary (Kathy) $15 000; shares of residual loss (Kathy $8 400, Steve $8 400)

# Chapter 9: Accounting for limited companies, co-operatives and non-profit organisations

1. C
2. A
3. C
4. A
5. D
6. A
7. B
8. C
9. D
10. D

**11. a.** **Two from:** limited liability for debts; greater opportunities to raise finance; indefinite life; separate legal identity, etc.

**b.** **Three from:** ordinary shares carry voting rights, preference shares do not; ordinary shares have variable dividends, preference shares have a fixed dividend; preference shares are appropriated their dividend ahead of any dividend to ordinary shareholders; in the event of a company failure preference shareholders take precedence over ordinary shareholders for the return of their investment.

**c.** Journal
**i.** Dr bank $600 000; Cr ordinary share capital $600 000
**ii.** Dr bank $500 000; Cr preference share capital $500 000

**12. a.** **Two from:** ordinary shares are part of the equity (they are capital), debentures are not (they are loans); the return on ordinary shares is variable, the return on debentures is fixed; dividends are recorded in the appropriation account, debenture interest is charged to the income statement; in the event of a company failure ordinary shareholders come after debenture holders for the return of their investment.

**b.** Income statement

Revenue $850 000 less cost of sales $492 000, gross profit $358 000

**Less expenses:** administration expenses $33 100, auditors' fees $8 800, debenture interest $24 000 (8% × $300 000), directors' remuneration $48 700, distribution and selling costs $20 500 ($21 200 less prepaid $700), depreciation of non-current assets $60 800 (20% × $304 000) (subtotal $195 900); net profit $162 100

c. Appropriation account

Net profit $162 100 less transfer to general reserve $75 000 less dividends $45 000 (subtotal $42 100) add retained earnings b/f $48 400; retained earnings at 31 December 2018, $90 500

**13. a.** Authorised capital is the maximum amount of capital that a limited liability company can issue.

**b.** Appropriation account (figures in $000s): profit for the year $402 less transfer to general reserve $220, less dividends paid $80, less proposed dividends $80 (20 cents x 400,000) (subtotal $22) plus opening retained earnings $135; closing retained earnings $157

**c.** Statement of financial position (figures in $000s)

**Non-current assets:** $1 770 less accumulated depreciation $300 (subtotal $1 470)

**Current assets:** inventory $57, accounts receivable $71 ($78 less provision for doubtful debts $7) rent prepaid $5, cash at bank $41 (subtotal $174)

**Current liabilities:** accounts payable $23, debenture interest due $10, dividends proposed $80 (subtotal $113)

**Non-current liabilities:** 10% debentures $200

Totals $1 331

**Equity:** ordinary share capital $800, general reserve $374 ($154 + $220) retained earnings $157 (subtotal $1 331)

**d.** Return on investment = net profit × 100/capital invested (shares + reserves at beginning of year) i.e. $402 × 100/Shares $800 + general reserve $154 + opening retained earnings $135 = $402 × 100/$1 089 = 36.91%

**14. a.** **Three from:** open membership; democratic control; limited interest on capital; patronage refund; continuous education; co-operation between co-operatives.

**b.** **Income and expenditure account income:** interest on investments $5 850 add membership fees $47 600 ($42 300 plus due $5 300) (subtotal $53 450)

**Expenditure:** administration costs $5 980, annual general meeting costs $2 240, auditors' remuneration $4 190, insurance $1 640 ($1 920 less prepaid $280), depreciation furniture and equipment $4 140 (15% × $27 600), depreciation premises $5 000 (4% × $125 000) (subtotal $23 190)

Surplus for year $30 260

**c.** Appropriation account

Surplus for year $30 260 less dividends paid $15 500, transfer to statutory reserve $9 078, secretary's honorarium $5 300 (subtotal $82) plus undistributed surplus b/f $38 900; closing undistributed surplus $38 982

**15. a.** Honorarium is a payment made to an official in a co-operative society as a sign of appreciation; the payment is instead of a wage or salary.

**b.** Appropriation account

Surplus for year $95 000 less dividends paid $35 000, honorarium $12 600, transfer to statutory reserve $19 000 (20% × $95 000) (subtotal $28 400) plus undistributed surplus b/f $39 600; closing undistributed surplus $68 000

**c.** Statement of financial position (balance sheet)

**Non-current assets:** cost $580 000 less accumulated depreciation $105 000; investments in other co-operatives $42 000 (subtotal $517 000)

**Current assets:** cash at bank $18 500 (subtotal $18 500)

**Current liabilities:** accounts payable $13 500, administration costs due $700, membership fees in advance $2 300 (subtotal $16 500)

**Total:** $519 000

**Capital and reserves:** share capital $370 000, statutory reserves $81 000 ($62 000 + $19 000), undistributed surplus $68 000 (subtotal $519 000)

**16. a.** The account will inform the committee of the liquid funds the club has available. The committee will be able to see the extent to which liquid funds have increased or decreased during the year, and the reasons for the change. The information will help the committee make important decisions about the management of the club.

**b.** Receipts and payments account

**Receipts:** opening balance of cash in hand and at bank $6 330 ($370 + $5 960) plus donations from local businesses $16 300, members subscriptions $35 350 [(180 + 22) × $175], proceeds from sale of old equipment $520, sales of refreshments $22 980 (subtotal $81 480)

**Expenditure:** clubhouse and sports ground rent $26 800, office expenses $2 750, new sports equipment $8 900, refreshment purchases $14 300, sports competition prizes $2 210, sports ground maintenance $11 680, travel costs for away fixtures $6 980, wages of refreshment staff $7 260 (subtotal $80 880); closing balances of cash in hand and at bank $600

## Chapter 10: Manufacturing and inventory control

| | | | | |
|---|---|---|---|---|
| **1.** A | **2.** B | **3.** D | **4.** C | **5.** B |
| **6.** C | **7.** C | **8.** D | **9.** C | **10.** D |

**11. a. i.** A direct cost is a cost which can be identified with a single unit of production, e.g. direct raw materials.

**ii.** An indirect cost is a cost which cannot be identified with a single unit of production, e.g. factory rent.

**b.** Manufacturing account for the year ended 31 December 2018

**Prime cost section:**

Opening inventory of raw materials $11 820 + purchases of raw materials $44 320 + carriage inwards on raw materials $860 (subtotal $57 000) less closing inventory of raw materials $14 390, subtotal cost of raw materials used $42 610; plus direct wages ($49 580 + accrual $2 800) $52 380; subtotal prime cost $94 990

**Factory overheads:**

Depreciation of factory machinery $8 350 + factory electricity $4 910 + factory insurance ($6 670 − prepayment 1/3 × $1 800) $6 070 + indirect wages and salaries $21 320 + machinery repairs and maintenance $1 830; subtotal $42 480

Adjustment for work in progress

Add opening inventory $6 290, less closing inventory $5 310, subtotal $980

**Cost of production: $138 450**

c. Income statement (trading section) for the year ended 31 December 2018
Revenue ($283 640 – sales returns $920) = $282 720
Less cost of sales of finished goods: opening inventory of finished goods $8 400 + cost of production $138 450 – closing inventory of finished goods $7 920; subtotal $138 930
Gross profit $143 790

12. a. Prime cost is the total of direct costs.

b. Manufacturing account for the year ended 31 October 2018
**Prime cost section:**
Opening inventory of raw materials $14 840 + purchases of raw materials ($92 660 – purchases returns $770) $91 890 (subtotal $106 730) less closing inventory of raw materials $15 090, subtotal cost of raw materials used $91 640; plus direct wages $112 300; subtotal prime cost $203 940

**Factory overheads:**
Insurance $5 650, factory supervisor's salary $24 320, depreciation of machinery $17 000, maintenance and repairs ($23 800 × 90%) $21 420, power charges ($9 260 + accrual $850) $10 110, rent [($24 800 – prepaid $1 300) × 60%] $14 100; subtotal $92 600

Adjustment for work in progress

Add opening inventory $1 890 less closing inventory $1 370; subtotal $520

Cost of production: $297 060

c. Income statement for the year ended 31 October 2018
Revenue $463 820 less cost of sales of finished goods (opening inventory $13 300 + cost of production $297 060 – closing inventory $12 260) $298 100; subtotal gross profit 165 720 less expenses [carriage outwards $1 110 + depreciation of furniture and equipment (15% × $14 500) $2 175 + maintenance and repairs ($23 800 × 10%) $2 380 + rent ($23 500 × 40%) $9 400; subtotal $15 065; net profit $150 655

d. Extract from statement of financial position (balance sheet) at 31 October 2018:
**Current assets:**
**Inventories:** raw materials $15 090 + work in progress $1 370 + finished goods $12 260; subtotal $28 720

e. **Cost of one unit:** cost of production $297 060/4 300 = $69.08

13. a. Work in progress is the value of partly completed products.

b. **Cost of one kayak:**
Direct materials (3.5 kg × $14.50) $50.75; direct labour (2.8 hrs × $12.20) $34.16; subtotal direct cost $84.91; total indirect costs per kayak ($1,500/30) $50; total $134.91

c. **Selling price:** cost $134.91 + mark-up (75% × $134.91) $101.18 = $236.09

d. **Profit on order:** 22 × $101.18 = $2 225.96

14. a. When indirect costs are allocated they are wholly given to a particular cost centre; when indirect costs are apportioned they are divided between cost centres on a rational basis.

b.  Cutting department

Allocated indirect costs $18 400 + share of rent ($16 800 × 4/5) $13 440 + share of wages of supervisors ($31 500 × 11/15) $23 100 = $54 940

Finishing department

Allocated indirect costs $13 200 + share of rent ($16 800 × 1/5) $3 360 + share of wages of supervisors ($31 500 × 4/15) $8 400 = $24 960

Overhead absorption rates

**Cutting department:** total indirect costs $54 940/5 500 = $9.99 per machine hour

**Finishing department:** total indirect costs $24 960/640 = $39 per labour hour

c.  Selling price of order

Direct materials (14 × $5.30) $74.20 + direct labour (5 × $12.50; 1.5 × $10.20) $77.80; subtotal total direct costs $152

**Indirect costs:** cutting department (6 × $9.99) $59.94 + finishing department (1.5 × $39) $58.50; subtotal total indirect costs $118.44

**Selling price:** total cost $270.44 + mark-up (50% × $270.44) $135.22 = $405.66

15. a.  **Inventory at end of March:** (15 @ $12 = $180; 10 @ $13 = $130) = $310
Inventory at end of December (3 @ $12 + $36; 10 @ $13 + $130) = $166

b.  **Inventory at end of August:** (40 @ $32 = $1 280; 30 @ $34 = $1 020) = $2 300
Inventory at end of December (40 @ $32 = $1 280; 3 @ $34 = $102) = $1 382

c.  **Inventory at end of July:** (20 @ $25 = $500; 40 @ $30 = $1 200), i.e. 60 items total value $1 700 so average cost per item is $1 700/60 = $28.333

**Inventory at end of December:** 32 items @ $28.333 each = $906.67

d.  FIFO produces the highest profit figures in a period when prices are rising.

# Chapter 11: Accounting for the entrepreneur

1.  A       2.  C       3.  D       4.  C       5.  C
6.  D       7.  B       8.  B       9.  A       10. D

11. a.  **Details should include:** name of employee, date of payslip, gross pay, statutory deductions such as income tax and national insurance, any voluntary deductions such as trade union subscriptions, net pay, date payment will be made, etc.

b.  **Monthly gross pay in 2017:** $7 250; 5% increase is $362.50

c.  **Gross pay for week:** $1 440 (40 × $36) + overtime $162 (3 × 1.5 × $36); total $1 602

d.  **Gross pay for week:** Jex ($4 × 22 = $88) + Kex ($7x 13 = $91) + Lex ($8 × 11 = $88); total $267

12. a.  **Information should include:** name of employee, date at end of week, hours in and out, total of normal working hours, total of any overtime hours each day, total of normal hours for week and total of any overtime hours for week.

b.  **Gross wage for week:** items accepted – Monday 484 + Tuesday 471 + Wednesday 514 + Thursday 483 + Friday 464, i.e. 2 416 items at $2.20 per item = $5 315.20

c.  **Gross salary for December 2018:** $3 150 + commission $640 (2% × $32 000), i.e. $3 790

13. a.  Statutory deductions are deductions from an employee's pay which an employer is legally required to make (for example, income tax); whereas voluntary deductions are those which

an employee requests an employer to make (for example, donations to a charity).

b. **Laurelle's net pay per month:** $8 500 ($102 000/12) gross pay less income tax $1 400 [(8 500 − monthly personal allowance $1 500) × 20%] less national insurance $340 ($8 500 × 4%) − pension scheme $255 ($8 500 × 3%) = $6 505

c. **Nico's net pay for a week:** gross pay $1 440 (40 × $32) + (4 × $40) less income tax $218.77 [20% × taxable pay ($1 440 less weekly personal allowance $346.15)] less national insurance $57.60 ($1 440 × 4%) less pension scheme $43.20 ($1 440 × 3%) less trade union contribution $12 = $1,108.43

14. a. **Business plan should include four of:** executive summary; company background; marketing plan; marketing analysis; financial plan.

b. Cash flow projections
**Month 1:** total receipts $37 500, total payments $34 600 (net + $2 900); opening balance $0; closing balance $2 900

**Month 2:** total receipts $6 000, total payments $6 600 (net − $600); opening balance $2 900, closing balance $2 300

**Month 3:** total receipts $7 000, total payments $6 600 (net + $400); opening balance $2 300; closing balance $2 700

**Month 4:** total receipts $13 000, total payments $14 900 (net − $1 900); opening balance $2 700, closing balance $800

**Month 5:** total receipts $9 000, total payments $6 900 (net + $2,100); opening balance $800, closing balance $2 900

**Month 6:** total receipts $9 000, total payments $6 900 (net + $2 100), opening balance $2 900; closing balance $5 000

15. a. **Executive summary should include:** the owner(s), type of business (sole trader, partnership, etc.) nature of the business, source of goods, cash or credit trading (or both), business hours, capital investment required, etc.

b. Sales budget:
**Month 1:** 200 units; $6 000
**Month 2:** 220 units; $6 600
**Month 3:** 242 units; $7 260

c. Production budget:
**Month 1:** 200 units + closing inventory 44 (20% × 220); 244 units
**Month 2:** deduct opening inventory 44 units + sales 220 + closing inventory 48 (20% × 240); 224 units
**Month 3:** deduct opening inventory 44 units + sales 240 + closing inventory 50 (20% × 250); 246 units

d. Cash flow projection
**Month 1:** receipts $46 000, payments $38 880 (including materials $1 952, labour $2 928); (net + $7 120); opening balance $0; closing balance $7 120
**Month 2:** receipts $6 600, payments $6 480 (including materials $1 792, labour $2 688); (net + $120); opening balance $7 120; closing balance $7 240
**Month 3:** receipts $7 260, payments $6 920 (including materials $1 968, materials $2 952); (net + $340); opening balance $7 240, closing balance $7 580

# Exam preparation

| | | | | |
|---|---|---|---|---|
| **1.** B | **2.** C | **3.** B | **4.** A | **5.** D |
| **6.** B | **7.** A | **8.** B | **9.** A | **10.** C |
| **11.** B | **12.** D | **13.** A | **14.** C | **15.** D |
| **16.** A | **17.** D | **18.** D | **19.** A | **20.** D |

**21. a.** Cash book

**Cash Dr:** 1st balance b/d 180, 8th sales $3 520

**Cash Cr:** 2nd drawings $170, 9th bank $2 400, 24th purchases $820, 31st balance c/d $310

**Discounts received:** 5th Lloyd's Wholesale Supplies $60, 21st Lloyd's Wholesale Supplies $123

**Bank Dr:** 1st balance b/d $770, 9th cash $2 400, 31st balance c/d $1 507

**Bank Cr:** 5th Lloyd's Wholesale Supplies $1 140, 11th office equipment $800, 21st Lloyd's Wholesale Supplies $2 337, 27th rent $400

(Note: Nov 1 Dr cash balance b/d 310; Cr bank balance b/d $1 507)

**b.** Lloyd's Wholesale Supplies

**Dr:** 5th bank $1 140, discounts received $70, 16th purchases returns $140, 21st bank $2 337, discounts received $123, 31st balance c/d $3 090

**Cr:** 1st balance b/d $1 200, 8th purchases $2 600, 23rd purchases $3 100

(Note: Nov 1 Cr balance b/d $3 090)

**c. i.** paying-in slip    **ii.** (cash) receipt

**22. a.** Reducing balance gives a higher figure for depreciation in the first years of a non-current assets use which corresponds with the higher amount of wear and tear suffered by the delivery vehicle. It also results in a more even charge against profits each year if it is recognised that service and repair costs on a delivery vehicle will be greater in the later years when depreciation charges are lower.

**b.** Income statement

Revenue $381 280 less sales returns $4 720 (subtotal $376 560) less cost of sales made up of opening inventory $17 200 add purchases $225 300 add carriage inwards $3 120 (subtotal $245 620) less closing inventory $18 400 (subtotal $227 220); gross profit $149 340 add income of discounts received $480 add interest on investments $1 400 ($1,190 + due $210) (subtotal $151 220) less expenses made up of administration expenses $14 830 add carriage outwards $4 450 add rent $22 300 add wages and salaries $44 300 add depreciation delivery vehicle $6 400 (20% × $32 000) add depreciation of furniture and equipment $2 550 (15% × $17 000) (subtotal of expenses $94 830); net profit $56 390

**c.** Accruals (matching) and prudence.

**d.** Net profit $56 390 × 100/net revenue $375 560 = 15.01%

**e.** Increase gross profit percentage on revenue (charging higher prices/reduced costs of goods from suppliers); better control of running costs.

**23. a.** **One of:** commission/omission/compensation/principle/original entry/complete reversal plus a suitable example

**b.** Journal

Dr general expenses $60, Cr suspense $60

Dr sales returns $190, Cr suspense $190

Dr suspense $540, Cr Grant Williams $540

**c.** Suspense account
Dr Grant Williams $540

Cr difference in TB totals $290, general expenses $60, sales returns $190

**d.** Cash flow projection
**January:** inflow sales $4000; outflows purchases $3000, expenses $700

**February:** inflow sales $4400, outflows purchases $3300, expenses $700

**March:** inflow sales $4840, outflows purchases $3630, expenses $700, bank loan repayment $2400

**Balances:**

**Opening balance:** January $900, February $1200, March $1600

**Closing balance:** January $1200, February $1600, March −$290

24. **a.** **Financial plan to include three of the following:** capital requirements; details of forecast revenue; costs; identification of suppliers; three-year financial forecasts of profits; cash flows.

**b.** Appropriation account
Net profit $87000 add interest on drawings $3680 (Michelle $1680, Nelson $2000) (subtotal $90680) less interest on capital $8000 (Michelle $3000, Nelson $5000) less salary Michelle $12000 (subtotal $70680); shares of remaining profits Michelle $42408, Nelson $28272

**c.** Nelson's current account
Dr interest on drawings $2000, drawings $25000, balance c/d $6272

Cr interest on capital $5000, share of remaining profit $28272

(Note: Dr balance b/d 1 January 2019, $6272)

**d.** **Gross pay:** $1422 [(35 × $36) + (3 × $54)] less income tax $244.40 [20% × $1422 less personal allowance per week $200)] less national insurance contribution $71.10 (5% × $1422) less health club $12; net pay $1094.50

25. **a.** Journal: Dr bank $1200000; Cr ordinary share capital $1200000
**b.** Statement of financial position (balance sheet)
**Non-current assets:** nbv $1402400

**Current assets:** inventory $63600, accounts receivable $53600, insurance prepaid $1200, cash at bank $41700 (subtotal $160100)

**Current liabilities:** accounts payable $38700, salaries due $3400, dividends proposed $120000 (subtotal $162100)

Total $1400 400

**Equity:** ordinary share capital $1200000, general reserve $122000 ($72000 + transfer $50000), retained earnings $78400 (total $1400400)

**c.** **Return on investment:** profit for year $255000/opening equity $1295400 (capital $1200000 + general reserve $72000 + retained earnings $23,400) i.e. 19.69%
**d.** Honorarium.

# Help all learners achieve their exam potential

✓ 100% matched to the CXC® syllabus meaning all essential material is covered

✓ Improve exam performance with sample answers and feedback

✓ Build assessment confidence and consolidate learning throughout the year with exam practice and tips

Find out more at www.oup.com/caribbean/cxc

 Study Guide

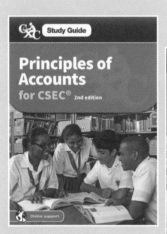

977 0 19 843731 4

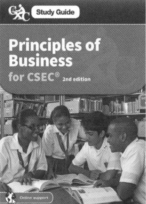

978 0 19 843739 0

978 1 4085 1643 0

978 1 4085 1655 2

OXFORD
UNIVERSITY PRESS